Prostaglandins

MEDICINAL CHEMISTRY
A Series of Monographs

EDITED BY

GEORGE deSTEVENS

CIBA Pharmaceutical Company
Division of CIBA Corporation
Summit, New Jersey

Volume 1. GEORGE deSTEVENS. Diuretics: Chemistry and Pharmacology. 1963

Volume 2. RUDOLFO PAOLETTI (ED.). Lipid Pharmacology. 1964

Volume 3. E. J. ARIËNS (ED.). Molecular Pharmacology: The Mode of Action of Biologically Active Compounds. (In two volumes.) 1964

Volume 4. MAXWELL GORDON (ED.). Psychopharmacological Agents. Volume I. 1964. Volume II. 1967

Volume 5. GEORGE deSTEVENS (ED.). Analgetics. 1965

Volume 6. ROLAND H. THORP AND LEONARD B. COBBIN. Cardiac Stimulant Substances. 1967

Volume 7. EMIL SCHLITTLER (ED.). Antihypertensive Agents. 1967

Volume 8. U. S. VON EULER AND RUNE ELIASSON. Prostaglandins. 1967

PROSTAGLANDINS

U. S. von Euler and Rune Eliasson

FYSIOLOGISKA INSTITUTIONEN I, STOCKHOLM, SWEDEN

1967

(AP) ACADEMIC PRESS   New York and London

ACADEMIC PRESS INC.
111 Fifth Avenue, New York, New York 10003

United Kingdom Edition published by
ACADEMIC PRESS INC. (LONDON) LTD.
Berkeley Square House, London W.1

LIBRARY OF CONGRESS CATALOG CARD NUMBER: 67-22778

PRINTED IN THE UNITED STATES OF AMERICA

Foreword

The many advances made in medicinal chemistry within the past quarter-century have done much to further our knowledge of the relationship between chemical structure and biological activity. This relationship has led to a tremendous collaborative effort between chemists and biologists, and this has been evidenced further by the considerable number of reviews that have appeared on various aspects of medicinal chemistry. For the most part, these have been confined to single chapters on selected topics. Of necessity, in such a format, it has been difficult to cover a particular area very broadly.

The purpose of this series is to present a series of monographs, each dealing with a specific field in medicinal chemistry. Thus, these edited or authored volumes will make available to the medicinal chemist and biologist an opportunity to review critically a topic; consequently, a broader perspective of a subject can be realized.

GEORGE deSTEVENS

Preface

The rapidly growing interest in prostaglandins is no doubt due mainly to their chemical identification and the availability of material sufficient for extensive studies. Since the 1930's when the highly potent principle in human semen was recognized to be a fatty acid with special properties until the isolation and chemical identification of the active factors by the brilliant work of Bergström and his associates some 25 years elapsed, illustrating how scientific progress moves in cycles, influenced by a variety of circumstances. The clarification of the structure of the prostaglandins paved the way for their biosynthesis, which, incidentally, was greatly aided by the availability of the natural precursors linolenic and arachidonic acids.

We are now witnessing an ever-growing accumulation of data obtained with the various prostaglandins in a large number of laboratories all over the world. A glance at the number of papers published in the last couple of years bears this out: 58 papers on the subject published in 1965 as opposed to 5 during 1960–1961. A comprehensive bibliography compiled by Dr. John E. Pike and Dr. James R. Weeks of the Upjohn Company in Kalamazoo, Michigan, generously placed at the disposal of those interested in the field, has proved to be a great help in surveying the literature. Two international symposia have been wholly or partially devoted to discussions on prostaglandins, the first held in Bristol, July 1965, and the second in Stockholm, June 1966, organized as a Nobel Symposium. The papers read at these meetings are available in published proceedings and supply detailed data on a variety of subjects within the field.

The chemical problems presented by the prostaglandins have obviously stimulated research and may yet lead to new and fruitful developments. It may be pertinent to recall, however, that the biological properties of the prostaglandins led to the detection of this group of substances, and the task of clarifying their biological and physiological roles in the organism still remains. That the prostaglandins are involved in mechanisms relevant to reproduction appears almost certain. Recent findings, however, hint at the possibility that this group of substances, like the catecholamines, are also of great significance in the regulation of lipolysis and in nerve transmission processes.

The present review, prepared at the request of Dr. G. deStevens, attempts to give a brief survey of the present state of prostaglandin research. The rapid accumulation of data makes errors of omission or commission almost inevitable, but it is our hope that this work will serve as an introduction to the field and will perhaps stimulate further research, the ultimate aim of which would be to establish the functional role of the prostaglandins.

We wish to express our sincere thanks to the publishers and authors for permission to use previously published material. Much of the work on the biological effects of prostaglandins by R. Eliasson was supported by liberal grants from the Swedish Medical Research Council, The Lalor Foundation, and the Population Council. We also wish to acknowledge, with gratitude, the generous gifts of pure prostaglandin preparations from Professor Sune Bergström and his group and from Dr. D. A. van Dorp. Finally, our thanks are due to Mrs. Britte Backman, Miss Ingrid Moos, and Mr. Nils-Åke Persson who helped prepare, with unfailing zeal and skill, the manuscript and illustrative material. The English has been kindly polished by Dr. deStevens.

Stockholm, Sweden　　　　　　　　　　U. S. VON EULER
October, 1967　　　　　　　　　　　　RUNE ELIASSON

Contents

Chapter 5/Relations of Prostaglandins to Other Lipid Acids Active on Smooth Muscle

Bibliography

1/Historical Survey

The first experiments that seemed to indicate the possibility of a substance with significant biological effects in the prostate gland of man were made by Battez and Boulet (1913) who observed that extracts of fresh human prostate tissue caused a strong depressor action on the blood pressure of dogs. The results are difficult to evaluate, however, since depressor effects were obtained with extracts of a variety of organs and might owe to the almost ubiquitously occurring histamine, choline and choline esters, or adenine compounds.

It seems appropriate, therefore, to date the first systematic studies of specific compounds in the male accessory glands to 1930 when Kurzrok and Lieb described some actions of human seminal fluid on isolated human uterus strips, no doubt guided by the idea that any action observed might have physiological significance. The authors then observed that human seminal fluid exerted an action consisting in either stimulation or relaxation. When studying the history of the patients from which the uterine strips were taken, they made the interesting observation that uteri from patients who had gone through successful pregnancies responded with relaxation, but uteri from women who had a history of complete or long-standing sterility were stimulated on addition of seminal fluid. The significance of this finding became clear only much later, particularly in the work of Eliasson and Bygdeman and their associates, but the observations of Kurzrok and Lieb gave, nevertheless, the first indications of a differentiated biological action of some constituent in human semen.

1

It is hardly surprising that the nature of the active principle was not recognized at that time, a time when the methods for identification of biologically active compounds were only beginning to be developed. Not unexpectedly, Cockrill *et al.* (1935) were considering acetylcholine as a possible candidate for the active compound, since this agent stood very much in the center of interest in those days following the fundamental observations by Dale, Feldberg, Gaddum, and others.

The new achievements in the pharmacological analysis of biologically occurring active substances, developed particularly by the flourishing British schools of pharmacology, revived the interest in the action of extracts of various organs and biological material on the whole. The proper use of specific inhibitors of the actions of some autopharmacologically active substances made it possible to differentiate biologically between various active compounds.

On a ground so prepared it was possible for Goldblatt (1933) to ascertain that the striking pharmacodynamical actions he discovered on adding human seminal plasma or extracts thereof to isolated organs, or by injection into the whole animal, owed to some principle that could be differentiated from the then known, generally occurring compounds. His findings were published in a rather modest way as a brief abstract in a journal little read by biologists.

Unaware of these observations and shortly afterwards, we published similar results with extracts of the vesicular gland of the sheep and with human seminal plasma (von Euler, 1934).

In his careful study Goldblatt (1935) described a variety of actions of the human seminal plasma including the interesting observation that the active principle sensitized the seminal vesicle of the guinea pig to adrenaline, a finding that was later amply confirmed and extended.

Starting with the findings that the vesicular gland of the sheep was a rich source of the active compound, we found it only natural to seek more information about its chemical nature. The observation that it could be extracted with lipid solvents from an acid solution but was freely water soluble in an alkaline medium not only suggested that it was of acidic character, but also provided a simple means of purification. It thus appeared to have the properties of a fatty acid, which was somewhat surprising since very little was known about biologically active substances of this kind and certainly nothing of their activity in the body.

Through the good offices of Hugo Theorell in the chemistry department of the Karolinska Institutet, who had just developed an apparatus for preparative electrophoresis allowing separation of various fractions, an active extract was separated. The results showed as expected that the active principle migrated toward the anode, as shown in Fig. 1.1.

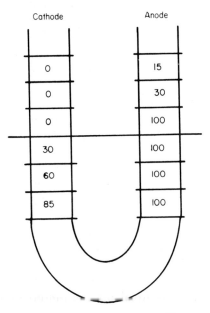

FIG. 1.1. Electrophoresis of a purified extract of human seminal fluid at pH 6.54 in the Theorell apparatus. Numbers denote the biological activities of the different segments (after von Euler, 1936).

Since it appeared that the active compound was a new and previously unknown chemical, it was thought that it should receive a name of its own. Owing to its occurrence in extracts of the prostate and vesicular gland, it was called prostaglandin.

Even though this name may not be entirely correct, since prostaglandin is produced primarily in the seminal vesicle as was later shown by Eliasson (1959), its use in the chemical literature has now become firmly established through the brilliant chemical work of Bergström and his associates.

With the methods at hand during the nineteen-thirties, further purification work was only moderately successful. It could be established, however, that prostaglandin was a nitrogen-free compound and that it probably was unsaturated. Its solubility properties further suggested that it possessed hydrophilic groups. Of some considerable value was the finding that it formed a stable and water-soluble barium salt that allowed its separation from large quantities of impurities. In these attempts at purification, great assistance was given by the I. G. Farben Company in Elberfeld, Germany, which prepared large batches of vesicular gland from the annual slaughter of thousands of Icelandic sheep. The purified preparation was subsequently used for various biological experiments, and since the barium salt was a dry and stable compound of high activity it was used as a biological standard. This preparation also served as a link between our early studies and the fundamental chemical work of Bergström and his group, who used this as starting material.

Thus Bergström and Sjövall succeeded in isolating an active compound from sheep glands in crystalline form (1960a). This was called prostaglandin F or PGF. It also became clear that prostaglandin was not a single substance, but consisted of a series of chemically related compounds of which the closely allied PGE corresponded in its action to most of the activity found in earlier extracts and of native human seminal fluid. In a remarkably short time Bergström and his associates, notably Sjövall and Samuelsson, were able to differentiate and isolate no less than 13 different compounds, all derivatives of a parent substance called prostanoic acid. The chemical structure having been revealed by ingenious work involving degradations and transformations, it appeared possible to synthesize the prostaglandin molecule by starting from an unsaturated fatty acid, arachidonic acid. This was achieved independently and simultaneously by the Bergström and van Dorp groups in Stockholm and Vlaardingen, respectively.

It is perhaps of some historical interest that the Eliasson discovery that a homogenate of sheep vesicular glands yielded increased amounts of active material on incubation raised the question of possible biosynthesis from a precursor in the incubation medium; among the substances tested were included arachidonic and linolenic acid. The biological tests available at that time did not permit proof that active material had been newly formed, however.

Although the earlier work was mainly concerned with the more readily observed effects of prostaglandin on circulation and on smooth muscle organs, later studies have revealed important effects on the central nervous system, mainly by British workers, and on metabolism, notably the lipolytic effect of sympathomimetic substances. The wide distribution of prostaglandins in a variety of organs also points out the possibility that this unique type of biologically active compound may have a more general significance than first anticipated. On the other hand, the relatively very high concentrations in the seminal fluid of man and a few animals suggest that some effect associated with the reproduction mechanisms is one of its basic actions in these species.

2/Chemistry

A. Isolation and Structure

1. EARLY OBSERVATIONS

Soon after its discovery it was shown that the biologically active principle occurring in human seminal fluid and in extracts of sheep vesicular glands was soluble in lipid solvents and of acidic character (von Euler, 1935a). Hence it appeared to be a new kind of biologically active substance and was named prostaglandin. By extracting an aqueous solution of prostaglandin under acidic conditions with ether or chloroform, the substance could be separated from a number of other known autopharmacologically active substances and at the same time purified to a considerable extent. Prostaglandin was readily extracted by aqueous alkali from the lipid solvents. On cataphoresis, the active substance migrated toward the anode (Fig. 1.1). The absorption spectrum of a purified solution of prostaglandin showed a maximum at 2750 Å (von Euler, 1936). After treatment of the oily residue from chloroform extracts with barium hydroxide, a large quantity of material remained as a soaplike residue although the barium salt was water soluble and could be desiccated to a dry resinlike material that over several years maintained its biological activity and served as a standard. The activity of this preparation was 12 units/mg or 1 unit in about 80 μg when tested on the rabbit jejunum (von Euler, 1939). One unit (prepared from human seminal fluid) on the same test preparation corresponded to 4–5 μg of PGE_1 (Bergström and von Euler, 1963). Comparative studies on the rabbit jejunum showed that 1 μg of the barium salt corresponded to about 0.1 μg of "PGE," but to a smaller amount on the rabbit blood pressure, suggesting that the barium salt consisted of a mixture of PGE and PGF.

In these early studies it was also shown that the most active preparations were nitrogen-free. Treatment with permanganate caused inactivation, as did catalytic hydrogenation, suggesting the presence of a double bond necessary for the activity.

High vacuum distillation yielded no active product. The moderately hydrophilic properties of prostaglandin suggested an hydroxylated fatty acid, which would also explain its poor solubility in petroleum ether (von Euler, 1936). From the data obtained it was concluded that the active principle was a lipid-soluble fatty acid that probably contained a double bond and a hydroxy group (von Euler, 1939).

The barium salt described above was partly used as material for the further purification experiments by Bergström (1949). By a series of procedures, including chromatography and counter-current distribution, the active principle was isolated in the form of the acetylated methyl ester with an activity of 475 units/mg; this, in the light of present knowledge, meant that a very high degree of purification was obtained. This was also indicated by the finding that the activity of the purified substance, which consisted of a colorless oil with an absorption maximum of 2800 Å paralleled the values for light absorption observed in Craig's countercurrent distribution. The methyl ester was slightly more active than the free acid. From these experiments it followed that the unit corresponded to approximately 2 μg of the active ester, which is in good agreement with the results obtained later with the pure compounds, when assayed on the rabbit jejunum. Acylation of the ester gave an inactive product that, after saponification, became active, but catalytic hydration caused irreversible inactivation.

2. ISOLATION OF PROSTAGLANDINS E AND F

The isolation of prostaglandin was announced in 1957 by Bergström and Sjövall. The active prostaglandin factor, which was termed PGF, was obtained in crystalline form. It had a melting point of 102°–103°C and was a nitrogen-free, unsaturated hydroxy acid. When its biological activity was tested on the isolated rabbit duodenum, it produced a good response in a concentration of about 5 ng/ml, which is in good agreement with later estimations (3–10 ng/ml) made by Bergström *et al.* (1959b).

In the report by Bergström and Sjövall (1957) it was also mentioned that at least one other active acidic factor was present in extracts of the sheep vesicular glands. This was of interest since it was found that the isolated prostaglandin factor PGF in moderate doses lacked effect on the rabbit blood pressure (Bergström and Sjövall, 1960a), while a fall was characteristic of all prostaglandin extracts prepared from biological material until then.

The material used for the preparation of PGF was vacuum-dried sheep vesicular glands stored over a period of several years at −20°C. All assays were made on the isolated rabbit duodenum. After extraction with about 70% ethanol and evaporation of the filtered extract to a twentieth of the original volume, the aqueous emulsion was acidified and repeatedly extracted with ether. From the ether solution the active compound was extracted with 0.2 *M* sodium phosphate buffer at pH 8 and sodium carbonate was added to maintain the pH level. After acidification of the buffer phases they were again extracted with ether that had been washed with small volumes of water. Upon evaporation, the ether left a dark brown, pasty residue that was subjected to countercurrent distribution between equal volumes of ether and 0.5 *M* phosphate buffer at pH 6.4. The buffer phases were acidified and extracted with ether. The most active phases (up to 20 μg/unit) were combined and subjected to reversed-phase partition chromatography. After equilibration of 10 volumes of 50% methanol–water with 1 volume of 50% isooctanol–chloroform, 4 ml of the less polar phase were supported on 4.5 gm of hydrophobic Supercel that was then slurried in the aqueous phase and transferred to a chromatography column. About 100 mg of the material, dissolved in a small quantity of the moving phase, were added to the column. The biologically active fractions were combined and used for spectrophotometric analysis after paper chromatography and isolation of active spots with the guidance of a strip sprayed with a 15% ethanolic solution of phosphomolybdic acid. On heating to 80°C, this strip revealed blue spots, one of which contained almost all of the activity. The phase system used for paper chromatography was 50:50 ethylene chloride–heptane as the moving phase equilibrated with an equal volume 80% acetic acid–water.

Further purification was achieved by a second partition chromatography using an acid solvent system, in which 3 volumes of 50:50 ethylene chloride–heptane were equilibrated with 1 volume of 60:40 acetic acid–water; this system was found to be suitable as a moving phase. Four milliliters of the acetic acid–water phase were supported on 4.5 gm of Hyflo Supercel and served as stationary phase. Material from the reversed-phase chromatography were run on this system.

Since the activity during subsequent paper chromatography was located in one spot with the phosphomolybdic reagent, spot tests with 20 μg of the effluent were used to detect the active fractions.

After evaporation of these *in vacuo* at 50°C the main fraction of the physiological activity crystallized partly in needle-shaped crystals. The crystals were relatively insoluble in ether but could be recrystallized from ethyl acetate–light petroleum until reaching a constant melting point of 102°–103°C. The elemental analysis corresponded to the formula $C_{20}H_{36}O_5$ (MW, 356.49), which agreed well with the result of titration in 50% ethanol, indicating a pK of 6.3 and an equivalent weight of 357 ($\pm$20). During microhydrogenation, slightly more than 1 mole of hydrogen was taken up per mole, assuming a molecular weight of 354.

After the isolation of the prostaglandin factor PGF, Bergström and Sjövall (1960b) soon announced the isolation of a second more lipid-soluble factor that lowers the blood pressure of various animals and is responsible for most of the biological activity in fresh or frozen sheep vesicular glands. This factor, which was termed PGE, was also obtained in crystalline form.

The preparative procedure was similar to that described for

PGF, but was modified in some respects. The frozen and minced glands were extracted with 4 volumes of 95% ethanol and the filtrate was prepared as with PGF. The extract was directly subjected to reversed-phase chromatography in the system used for PGF; the stationary phase was supported on Hostalen (Hoechst). A 10–30-fold purification was obtained in this way. In order to separate the blood pressure-lowering PG factor from PGF, the reversed-phase chromatography was performed a second time. In this, 35% methanol–water was saturated with 0.1 volume of 40% isoamyl acetate–chloroform as moving phase. The hydrophobic phase was used as the stationary phase and supported on silane-treated kieselguhr. No activity owing to PGF was found, since this compound is eluted just after the front.

When paper chromatographed, PGE moved somewhat faster than PGF and was separated from it. Column chromatography with acid solvent systems was not successful, however, in separating PGE and PGF. In the paper chromatograms, the highest PGE activity was found in the last part of the activity peak. The last half of the active band obtained from the second reversed-phase chromatography was therefore collected, evaporated to dryness, and dissolved in ethyl acetate. In contrast to the first half of the band, needle-shaped crystals were obtained in the last half. After recrystallization from ethyl acetate and ethyl acetate–heptane, a constant melting point of 115°–117°C was reached. The analysis corresponded to the formula $C_{20}H_{34}O_5$ with a molecular weight of 354.5. Figure 2.1 shows the infrared spectrum of the methyl ester of PGE (later designated PGE_1).

Soon afterwards it was demonstrated (Bergström *et al.*, 1962a) that reduction of PGE with sodium borohydride yielded two compounds, one of which was identical with the previously isolated PGF while the other differed in its physical and chemical properties but had the same elemental composition. The first isolated compound was designated PGF_1 and the second compound PGF_2. These compounds were later designated $PGF_{1\alpha}$ and $PGF_{1\beta}$ (Bergström *et al.*, 1963a). After reduction with sodium borohydride, paper chromatography showed that the original spot of PGE had been replaced by two new spots. The phase system consisted of equal parts of ethylene chloride and heptane as the moving phase and 70% acetic acid as the stationary phase. The R_f values, taking that of PGE as 1.00, were 0.72 and 0.55, respectively; the first one was identical with that of PGF isolated from sheep vesicular gland.

The two PGF compounds ($PGF_{1\alpha}$ and $PGF_{1\beta}$) were separated by reversed-phase partition chromatography. From a melting point determination, the X-ray diffraction powder pattern, the mass spectrum, and the infrared spectrum, it became evident that the more slowly moving factor was identical with $PGF_{1\alpha}$. The faster-moving factor, $PGF_{1\beta}$, as well as $PGF_{1\alpha}$, could be crystallized from ethyl acetate–pentane.

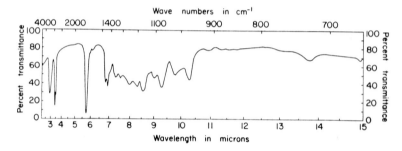

FIG. 2.1. Infrared spectrum of the methyl ester of PGE_1 made in a KBr disc (after Bergström and Sjövall, 1960b).

3. STRUCTURE OF PROSTAGLANDINS

The number of hydroxyls per methyl ester group was determined for PGE, $PGF_{1\alpha}$, and $PGF_{1\beta}$ and showed that $PGF_{1\alpha}$ and $PGF_{1\beta}$ each had approximately three hydroxyl groups. Mass spectrometric analysis was carried out after methylation of the methyl esters and purification by gas chromatography. The mass spectrograms are almost identical for the two PGF compounds, corresponding to the trimethyl ethers (MW, 412). The peaks seen in the mass spectrogram from PGE indicate a dimethyl ether (MW, 396). The data conform with the successive loss of one and two molecules of methanol (MW, 32), respectively, from the dimethyl ether of PGE methyl ester, and of 3 molecules from the trimethyl ethers. All compounds seem to contain an easily detached group with a molecular weight of 71.

Compound $PGF_{1\beta}$ was found to be considerably less active on rabbit intestine, having only 10–20% of the activity of $PGF_{1\alpha}$ (Bergström *et al.*, 1962a).

From these studies it emerged that PGE differs from PGF_1 in that it has a carbonyl grouping that can be reduced to the corresponding alcohol, as in $PGF_{1\alpha}$. At the same time the stereoisomeric alcohol $PGF_{1\beta}$ is formed. In agreement with this it was found that PGE gave a positive spot test for carbonyl with nitrophenylhydrazine. From the wavelengths in the infrared (IR) spectrum for the strong band in the carbonyl region, it was held probable that a cyclopentanone might be present; this later was shown to be the case.

The disappearance of the band at 10.30 μ (971 cm^{-1}) on hydrogenation in all three compounds indicated that the double bond had the trans configuration, and the lack of absorption in the 210–250-mμ region indicated that it was not in conjugation with the carbonyl or carboxyl group.

The quantitative acylation experiments indicated that the F compounds contain three hydroxyls. It was also concluded that the compounds contain one ring.

The data thus indicated the presence of the groups shown in the following tabulation.

PGE	$PGF_{1\alpha}$ and $PGF_{1\beta}$[a]
$C_{20}H_{34}O_5$	$C_{20}H_{36}O_5$
1 Carboxyl	1 Carboxyl
1 Carbonyl (cyclopentanone)	—
2 Hydroxyls	3 Hydroxyls
1 Double bond (trans)	1 Double bond (trans)
1 Ring	1 Ring

[a] In the paper named PGF_1 and PGF_2 (Bergström *et al.*, 1962a).

From these data and the results of a series of degradations, the formulas of PGE and PGF could be computed (Bergström *et al.*, 1962b). Most of the identifications were made with the aid of mass spectrography (MS) and by gas–liquid chromatography (GLC), and were checked through synthesis and comparison with the mass spectrograms of the synthetic compounds. The final elucidation of the side chains was made with the aid of an ingenious set of procedures described in detail by Bergström *et al* (1963b).

Treatment of PGE with sodium hydroxide (0.5 N) at room temperature caused a loss of one hydroxyl group and transformed it into a compound with absorption at 278 mμ. Oxidative ozonolysis of the methyl ester acetate of this compound yielded suberic acid, succinic acid, and α-hydroxyheptanoic acid, which accounted for 19 of the 20 carbon atoms.

Catalytic reduction of the methyl ester of PGE in ethanol gave a dihydro compound that, on alkali treatment, yielded a product with one less hydroxyl group that absorbed at 237 mμ. Oxidative ozonolysis yielded suberic acid and 4-keto-7-hydroxydodecanoic acid, which accounted for all 20 carbon atoms.

The compound with saturated side chains obtained on catalytic reduction of PGE with platinum was isolated and identified, allowing the following provisional formula to be set up for PGE: 2-(6-carboxyhexyl)-3-(3-hydroxyocten-1-yl)-4-hydroxycyclopentanone (see Fig. 2.2). The IUPAC notation (1961) is: A5(C_8EIQ3)1(7C_7X)2EQ3Q5. The C_{20} parent compound with the formula shown in Fig. 2.2 has been given the trivial name of prostanoic acid.

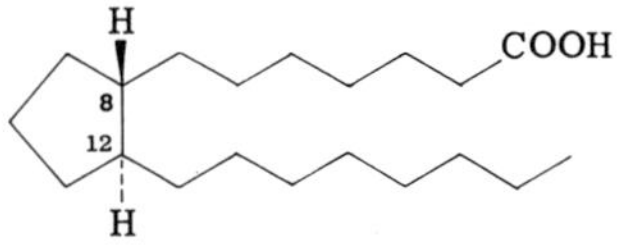

Prostanoic acid

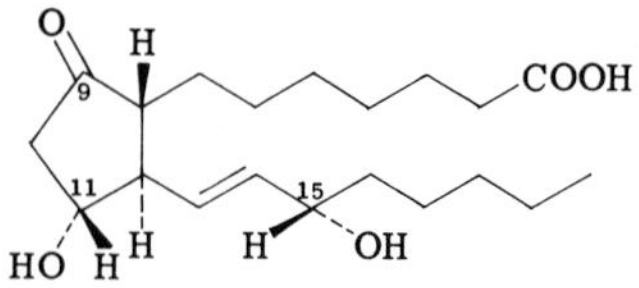

PGE₁

FIG. 2.2. Structural formulas of prostanoic acid and PGE₁ (after Nugteren *et al.*, 1966a).

The structural formula for compound F_2 was confirmed by a three-dimensional single crystal analysis of the tri-*p*-bromo-benzoate of the methyl ester, which also gave the stereochemistry of the molecule (Fig. 2.3). The derivative used was orthorhombic *(P2,2,2,)* with $a = 26.14$, $b = 33.93$, and $c = 4.76$ Å (Abrahamsson *et al.*, 1963).

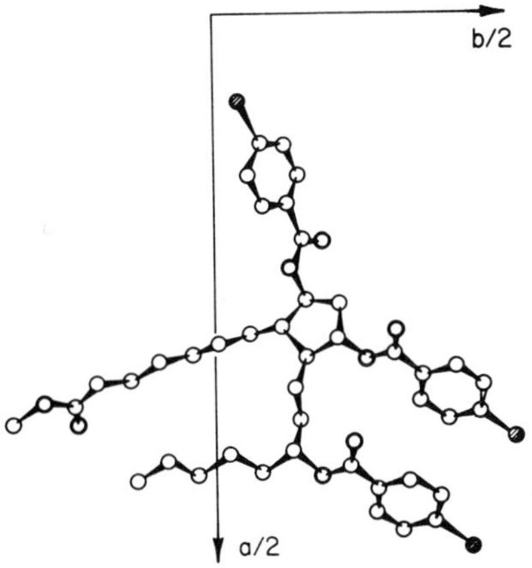

Fig. 2.3. Scale drawing of the tri-*p*-bromobenzoate of the methyl ester of compound PGF₂ in the correct absolute configuration; deduced from the electron density map (after Abrahamsson *et al.*, 1962).

4. The Absolute Configuration of the Prostaglandins

The earlier formulas representing the prostaglandins were based on X-ray analysis and the measurement of optical rotation in small amounts. It was later established (Nugteren *et al.*, 1966a), however, that the absolute configuration should be represented by the formulas in Fig. 2.2.

The conclusion was based on the finding that the 11-hydroxy-12,14-eicosadienoic acid formed by the PG-synthesizing system probably has the L-configuration. Although it had earlier been assumed that the 2-hydroxyheptanoic acid was the D-form, it could be established in later experiments that the product obtained from PGE₁ had the L-configuration. PGE₁ is thus levo-rotatory and shows a strong negative Cotton effect at about 300 nm during optical rotatory dispersion (ORD) in methanol

(C, 0.14), 20°C; α_{589}, $-58°$; α_{315}, $-2120°$ (trough); α_{276}, $+2060°$ (peak).

By substituting the formulas used in previous publications for their mirror images, the α and β nomenclature can be retained for the ring substituents. If prostanoic acid is given the structure and configuration shown in Fig. 2.2, the systematic name of PGE$_1$ is $(-)11\alpha,15$-S-dihydroxy-9-oxo-13-*trans*-prostenoic acid using the Cahn-Ingold-Prelog convention.

The F compounds shown in Fig. 2.4 differ from the E compounds only by the hydroxyl formed by reduction of the carbonyl in the ring.

A detailed account of the degradation processes leading to the elucidation and deduction of the structures of PGE$_1$, PGF$_{1\alpha}$, and PGF$_{1\beta}$ has been given in the paper by Bergström *et al.* (1963b).

5. PROSTAGLANDINS E$_2$ AND E$_3$

Further fractionations of the material from which PGE$_1$ was crystallized showed the presence of two new homogeneous but noncrystalline compounds, which were named E$_2$ and E$_3$ (Bergström *et al.*, 1962c). These could be separated from PGE$_1$ by paper chromatography.

In the same way that PGE$_1$ yielded two isomeric trihydroxy acids on reduction with sodium borohydride, PGE$_2$ and PGE$_3$ each yielded a pair of similar reduction products, designated PGF$_{2\alpha}$, PGF$_{2\beta}$, PGF$_{3\alpha}$, and PGF$_{3\beta}$.

The mobilities on paper chromatograms using 1:1 ethylene chloride–heptane as the moving phase and 70% acetic acid as the stationary phase relative to the corresponding PGE compounds (PGE$_1$ = 1.00) are given below.

PGE$_1$ (1.00)	PGF$_{1\alpha}$ (0.64) PGF$_{1\beta}$ (0.44)
PGE$_2$ (0.90)	PGF$_{2\alpha}$ (0.60) PGF$_{2\beta}$ (0.39)
PGE$_3$ (0.76)	PGF$_{3\alpha}$ (0.60) PGF$_{3\beta}$ (0.37)

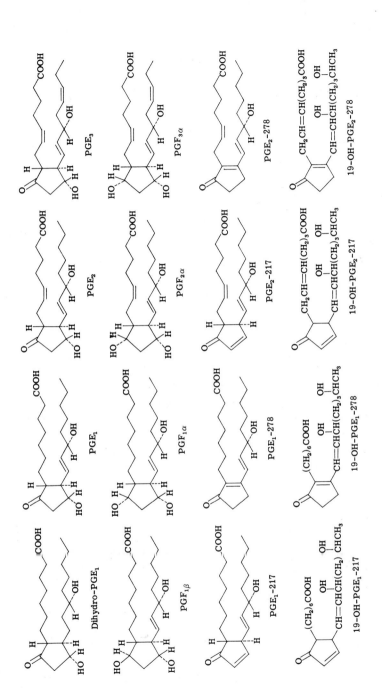

FIG. 2.4. Structural formulas of PGE and PGF compounds.

Mass spectra of the methyl esters of PGE₁–PGE₃ are given in Fig. 2.5.

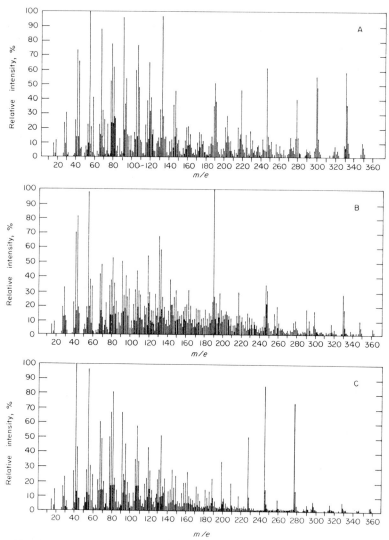

FIG. 2.5. Mass spectra of the PGE methyl esters: A, PGE₁ at 225°C; B, PGE₂ at 225°C; and C, PGE₃ at 250°C (after Bergström *et al.*, 1962c).

From mass spectrographic and other data it was concluded that the new compounds, PGE_2 and PGE_3, had the same basic structure as PGE_1 but that PGE_2 has one more double bond, located as indicated on Fig. 2.4. PGE_3 has two additional double bonds, the second one as in PGE_2 and the third one in the terminal pentyl group. The two F compounds formed from each member of the E series are two stereoisomeric alcohols formed through reduction of the keto group in the ring.

The structure of PGE_3 has been further corroborated by nuclear magnetic resonance studies on deuterochloroform solutions of the methyl ester with tetramethylsilane as the standard (Samuelsson, 1963c) (Fig. 2.6).

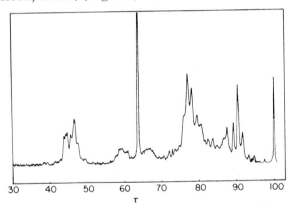

FIG. 2.6. Proton NMR spectrum of the methyl ester of prostaglandin E_3 (after Samuelsson, 1963c).

Like PGE_1, both PGE_2 and PGE_3 lower the blood pressure and stimulate the rabbit intestine, although the relative activities differ from that of PGE_1 (Bergström and von Euler, 1963).

6. PROSTAGLANDINS A_1 AND B_1 (PGE_1-217 AND PGE_1-278)

By treatment with alkali, PGE_1 loses one molecule of water. The resulting compound, which has been isolated and crystallized, has a molar extinction at 278 mμ of 23,000 and was first named PGE-278 (Fig. 2.4). It has recently been suggested that compound PGE_1-217 should be named PGA_1 and PGE_1-278 named PGB_1. The same applies to PGE_2 and 19-OH compounds.

The previous and present names are given in Table 2.I (Hamberg and Samuelsson, 1966, 1967).

TABLE 2.I

Old nomenclature	New nomenclature[a]
PGE_1-217	PGA_1
PGE_2-217	PGA_2
PGE_1-278	PGB_1
PGE_2-278	PGB_2
19-OH-PGE_1-217	19-OH-PGA_1
19-OH-PGE_1-278	19-OH-PGB_1

[a] After Hamberg and Samuelsson, 1967.

The formation of the derivatives PGE-278, PGE-237, and PGE-220 is illustrated in Fig. 2.7 and their degradation by oxidative ozonolysis in Fig. 2.8. The results were checked by synthesis of some of the degradation products and comparison of their mass spectrometric data. The physical data on the derivatives PGE-278, PGE-237, and PGE-220 of PGE_1 and the identification of their degradation products have established the structure of the side chains in PGE_1, their attachment to the ring, and the position of the keto group. By various procedures data were obtained allowing the deduction that the ring hydroxyl must be situated at the secondary carbon atom in the β position to the keto group which thus possesses a β-ketol structure.

As mentioned above, the prostaglandins from the E series have a λ_{max} at 278 mμ on treatment with sodium hydroxide. The chromophore consists of a conjugated dienone that is formed by the loss of the hydroxyl group at C-11 and subsequent isomerization of the introduced double bond to the Δ^{12} position as shown by Bergström et al. (1963a). A search for compounds in human seminal plasma that contain the dienone chromophore or can be converted into it by treatment with sodium hydroxide has been made by Hamberg and Samuelsson (1966, 1967). By these studies it became possible to isolate and establish the chemical structures of eight additional prostaglandins in human seminal fluid. These are given in Fig. 2.4. Using the new nomenclature (cf.

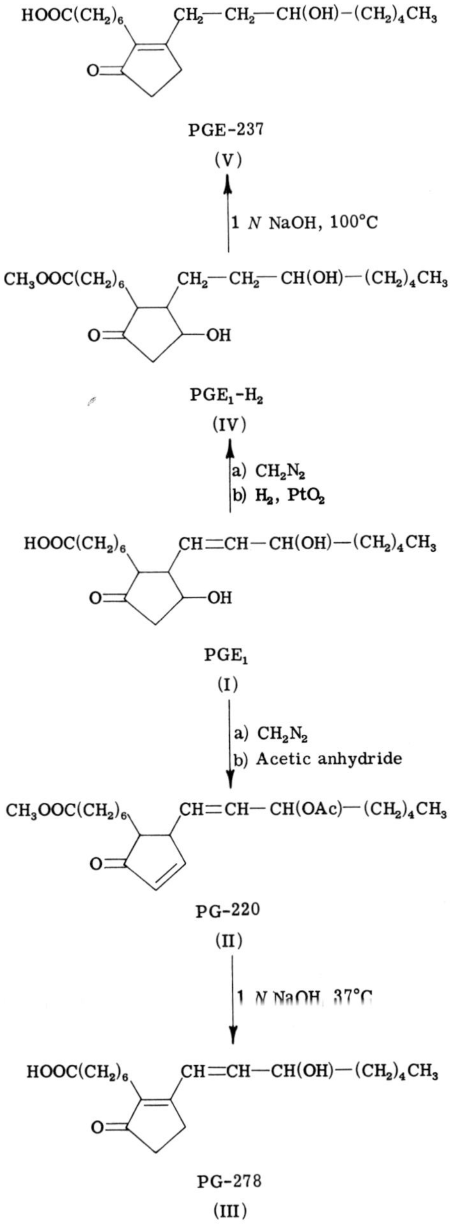

HOOC(CH$_2$)$_6$ CH$_2$—CH$_2$—CH(OH)—(CH$_2$)$_4$CH$_3$

O

PGE-237

(V)

↑

1 N NaOH, 100°C

CH$_3$OOC(CH$_2$)$_6$ CH$_2$—CH$_2$—CH(OH)—(CH$_2$)$_4$CH$_3$

O═   ─OH

PGE$_1$-H$_2$

(IV)

↑

a) CH$_2$N$_2$
b) H$_2$, PtO$_2$

HOOC(CH$_2$)$_6$ CH═CH—CH(OH)—(CH$_2$)$_4$CH$_3$

O═   ─OH

PGE$_1$

(I)

a) CH$_2$N$_2$
b) Acetic anhydride

↓

CH$_3$OOC(CH$_2$)$_6$ CH═CH—CH(OAc)—(CH$_2$)$_4$CH$_3$

O═

PG-220

(II)

1 N NaOH, 37°C

↓

HOOC(CH$_2$)$_6$ CH═CH—CH(OH)—(CH$_2$)$_4$CH$_3$

O

PG-278

(III)

FIG. 2.7. Formation of PGE-237 and PG-278 from PGE$_1$ (after Bergström *et al.*, 1963a).

Table 2.I) the compounds are designated as follows: PGA$_1$; PGA$_2$; PGB$_1$; PGB$_2$; 19-hydroxy-PGA$_1$; 19-hydroxy-PGA$_2$; 19-hydroxy-PGB$_1$; 19-hydroxy-PGB$_2$.

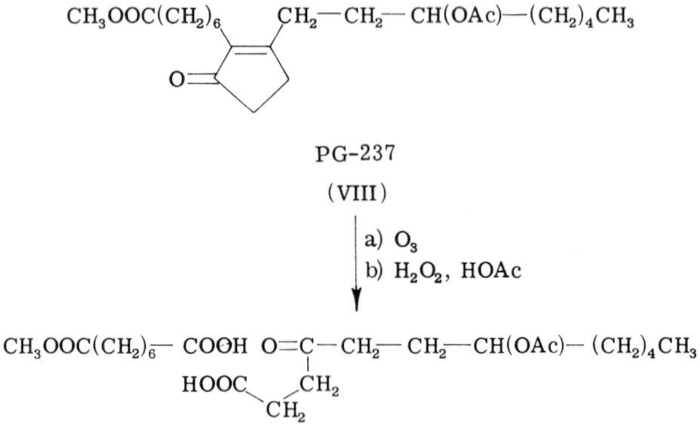

$$CH_3OOC(CH_2)_6 \qquad CH_2—CH_2—CH(OAc)—(CH_2)_4CH_3$$

PG-237

(VIII)

a) O$_3$
b) H$_2$O$_2$, HOAc

$$CH_3OOC(CH_2)_6— COOH \quad O=C—CH_2—CH_2—CH(OAc)—(CH_2)_4CH_3$$
$$HOOC \diagdown \diagup CH_2$$
$$CH_2$$

FIG. 2.8. Ozonolysis of PG-237 (after Bergström *et al.*, 1963a).

7. NOR-PGE$_1$

By removing one CH$_2$ unit from the side chain containing the carboxyl group in PGE$_1$, nor-PGE$_1$ is formed (MP, 89°C). Some biological properties have been described by Horton and Main (1966a, see Chapter 4).

B. Separation Procedures

1. SILICIC ACID CHROMATOGRAPHY

The discovery of a series of different prostaglandins in biological material by Bergström and co-workers made it urgently necessary to find a method to separate them in a simpler way. It had previously been found that descending paper chromatography separated the different PGE compounds, whereas there was hardly any separation of the members of the PGF series.

The technique for separation of the PGE and PGF compounds by silicic acid chromatography has been described by Bygdeman and Samuelsson (1964, 1966).

The silicic acid (Mallinckrodt, 100 mesh) was activated at 115°C and an amount of 1 gm prepared with ethyl acetate–

benzene (45:55). The column was eluted with increasing concentrations of ethyl acetate from ethyl acetate–benzene (45:55)
and 95:5 reservoirs of 30 ml each. Aliquots of the 1-ml fractions
were assayed for radioactivity from tritium-labeled PGE_1. The
residues after evaporation of the solvent under reduced pressure were then further processed by thin-layer chromatography.
The group separation on silica gel is necessary in order to allow
subsequent separation by thin-layer chromatography (Fig. 2.9).

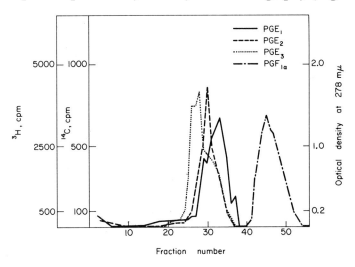

FIG. 2.9. The separation of the PGE compounds and $PGF_{1\alpha}$ by silicic acid
chromatography. Tracer amounts of ^{14}C-labeled PGE_1, ^3H-PGE_2, and ^3H-$PGF_{1\alpha}$
were used with 1 mg of PGE_3 (after Bygdeman and Samuelsson, 1966).

2. THIN LAYER CHROMATOGRAPHY

By using silica gel containing silver nitrate (Barret *et al.*,
1962) in thin-layer chromatography (TLC) it has been possible
to separate a large number of derivatives of PG with different
degrees of unsaturation (Gréen and Samuelsson, 1964). The
technique has been found useful both for analytical and preparative purposes. The solvent systems used were:

M I   Benzene–dioxane (5:4)
M II   Ethyl acetate–methanol–water (8:2:5)

M III   Ethyl acetate–methanol–water (16:2.5:10)
A I   Benzene–dioxane–acetic acid (20:20:1)
A II   Ethyl acetate–acetic acid–methanol–
         2,2,4-trimethylpentane–water
         (110:30:35:10:100)

Figure 2.10 shows the PG spots using solvent system A II.

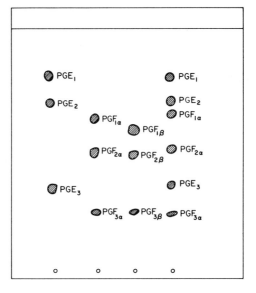

FIG. 2.10. Separation of prostaglandins as free acids with solvent system A II (after Gréen and Samuelsson, 1964).

All the six F compounds used in the tests were made by sodium borohydride reduction of the corresponding E compounds. Prostaglandins B_1–B_3 were prepared by alkali treatment of the corresponding E compound, as described above, and were separated as methyl esters with solvent system M III. The methyl esters can be separated in a similar way using solvent systems M I and M II.

The prostaglandins were extracted with methanol from the silica gel and the methyl esters were reextracted with chloroform after evaporation of the solvents; this gave a recovery of

90–95%. Free acids were extracted with ether after dilution with water and acidification with a recovery of 80–90%.

The modified technique according to Bygdeman and Samuelsson (1966) is as follows. The silica gel (Silica Gel G, E. Merck A. G., Germany) was washed twice with hot methanol and acetone and dried at 40°C for 12 hours and at 110°C for 2 hours. The plates were coated with a 0.25-mm layer of 25:1 silica gel and silver nitrate, and activated at 110°C for 30 minutes. Samples were applied with reference samples (10 μg each of E_1, E_2, and E_3) on both sides. The solvent system was ethyl acetate–acetic acid–2,2,4-trimethylpentane–water (110:20:30:100) equilibrated for 1 hour.

The reference samples were detected by spraying with 2,4-dinitrophenyl hydrazine (100 mg in 10 ml of concentrated HCl and 90 ml of ethanol) while the rest of the plate was covered. The corresponding compounds in the middle section were removed by suction and extracted twice with 1.5 ml of ethanol.

Of the extract, 1.5 ml was treated with 0.5 ml of a 2 N ethanolic solution of KOH and heated at 50°C for 25 minutes. Precipitated silver salts were removed by centrifugation, and ultraviolet absorption peak occurred at 278 mμ. The blank consisted of an ethanol extract of an empty area of a TLC plate and was treated in the same way.

3. Gas–Liquid Chromatography

Gas–liquid chromatography (GLC) of methyl esters or their acetates of the PGF group separated $PGF_{1\alpha}$ from those containing two or three double bonds but not the two latter compounds. Gas chromatography of the PGE compounds in all cases caused at least partial degradation (Gréen and Samuelsson, 1964).

In the subsequently developed technique (Bygdeman and Samuelsson, 1966) for the separation of the F compounds, a Pye Argon Chromatograph modified for use with a 2 m × 5 mm U-tube column and equipped with separately heated flash heater and argon ionization detector was used. Cyclohexanedimethanol polysuccinate (Applied Science Lab) at a concentration of 0.5%

was applied on 100–120 mesh acid-washed and silanized Gas-Chrom P: flash heater temperature, 200°C; column temperature, 184°C; detector temperature, 200°C; detector voltage, 1250 V; argon pressure, 1.4 kg/cm². The PGF fraction was treated with diazomethane and converted to trimethylsilyl ether derivatives, dissolved in 1 ml of dry tetrahydrofuran and 0.2 ml of hexamethyldisilazane, and 0.1 ml of trimethylchlorosilane was added. After 16 hours at room temperature the samples were centrifuged and the supernatant was extracted twice with hexane. After evaporation to dryness and redissolution in hexane, an aliquot was injected into the chromatograph and the area under each peak was measured. A faster procedure for preparation of the trimethylsilyl ether derivatives was to treat the PGF fraction with 0.5 ml of pyridine, 0.06 ml of hexamethyldisilazane, and 0.03 ml of trimethylchlorosilane. After 15 minutes at room temperature the sample was evaporated to dryness *in vacuo*.

C. Biosynthesis

1. FORMATION FROM DIHOMO-γ-LINOLENIC AND ARACHIDONIC ACIDS

After elucidation of the structure of PGE_1, PGE_2, and PGE_3 by Bergström and his associates it appeared possible to achieve biosynthesis by cyclization of dihomo-γ-linolenic acid, arachidonic acid, and 5,8,11,14,17-eicosapentaenoic acid, respectively. The same project was under way at the Unilever Research Laboratories in Vlaardingen and the successful attempts to synthesize PGE_2 from arachidonic acid were published in two papers appearing simultaneously (van Dorp *et al.*, 1964a; Bergström *et al.*, 1964a) (Fig. 2.11).

Biosynthesis was carried out with sheep vesicular glands as enzymic material. The glands were homogenized in a modified Bucher medium and 5 ml of the whole homogenate (1:2) was used with 0.4 mg of tritiated arachidonic acid. The mixture was incubated aerobically for 1 hour at 38°C. After the completion of the incubation, the contents were extracted with ethanol, taken up in ether, and chromatographed on a column of hydrophobic

Hyflo Supercel in solvent system M III after addition of PGE$_1$ and PGE$_2$. After treatment with NaOH the radioactivity eluted from the column coincided with the absorbancy curve of PGE$_2$ read at 278 mμ showing that this compound had been formed during the procedure. The yield of labeled PGE$_2$ from arachidonic acid was calculated to be about 20%. A sample subjected to thin-layer chromatography showed the same mobility as the sample of authentic PGE$_2$ (Bergström *et al.*, 1964a).

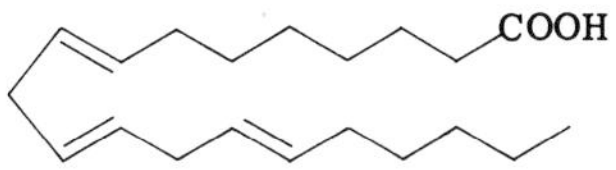

(I) 8,11,14-Eicosatrienoic
(dihomo-γ-linolenic acid)

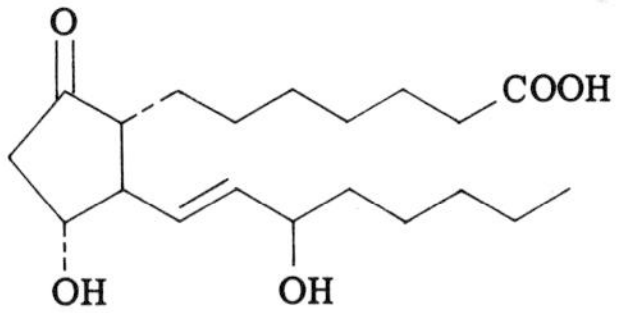

11α, 15-Dihydroxy-9-ketoprost-
13-enoic acid (prostaglandin E$_1$)

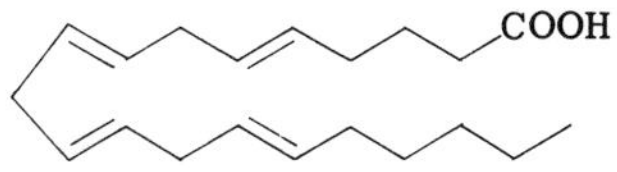

(II) 5,8,11,14-Eicosatetraenoic
acid (arachidonic acid)

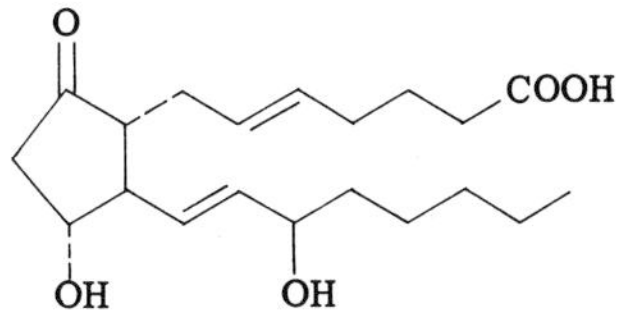

Prostaglandin E$_2$

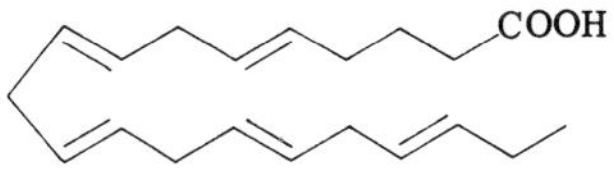

(III) 5,8,11,14,17-
Eicosapentaenoic acid

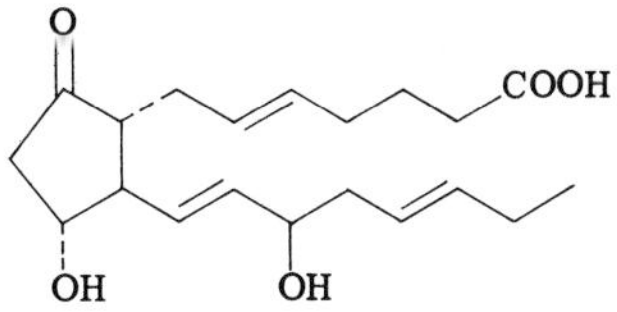

Prostaglandin E$_3$

FIG. 2.11. Formation of PGE$_1$, PGE$_2$, and PGE$_3$ from precursors (after Bergström *et al.*, 1964a).

The enzymic conversion of dihomo-γ-linolenic acid and all-cis-5,8,11,14,17-eicosapentaenoic acid to PGE_1 and PGE_3, respectively, was subsequently achieved (Bergström et al., 1964b) (Fig. 2.11). For the conversion to PGE_1, dihomo-γ-linolenic acid-2-^{14}C prepared from γ-linolenic acid (6,9,12-octadecatrienoic acid) and diethyl malonate-2-^{14}C was used. The conversion of all-cis-5,8,11,14,17-eicosapentaenoic acid into PGE_3 was shown to occur by determining the net formation of PGE_3 after addition of the unlabeled pentaenoic acid that was later conformed with ^{14}C-pentaenoic acid prepared from ^{14}C-labeled acetate in Euglena gracilis (Änggård and Samuelsson, 1965a).

Conversion of dihomo-γ-linolenic acid to PGE_1 was also achieved by van Dorp et al. (1964b), who also demonstrated that nor-PGE_1 and nor-PGE_2 were formed from all-cis-7,10,13-nonadecatrienoic acid and all-cis-4,7,10,13-nonadecatetraenoic acid, respectively. A precursor having 18 carbon atoms, such as all-cis-6,9,12-octadecatrienoic acid apparently was not a substrate for this enzyme system, since no conversion was obtained.

The occurrence of $PGF_{2\alpha}$ and PGE_2 in sheep lung (Änggård, 1965) made it appear possible that these compounds are biosynthesized in the lung tissue. This was also demonstrated by van Dorp (1966a,b), although he obtained a low yield. Other experiments (Änggård and Samuelsson, 1965a; Änggård et al., 1965) have shown that homogenates of guinea pig lung transform tritium-labeled arachidonic acid into $PGF_{2\alpha}$ and PGE_2, although by different pathways for the two compounds (Fig. 2.12).

All three oxygen atoms that are incorporated during biosynthesis derive from molecular oxygen (Ryhage and Samuelsson, 1965; Samuelsson, 1965a; and Nugteren and van Dorp, 1965). The oxygen atoms at C-9 and C-11 originate from the same oxygen molecule, suggesting an intermediate with a cyclic peroxide between C-9 and C-11. The breaking up of this cyclic peroxide might occur with a change in the state of oxidation, leading to PGE_1 or, by reduction, to $PGF_{1\alpha}$ (Samuelsson, 1965a). This would explain why no interconversion occurs between PGE_2 and $PGF_{2\alpha}$ during their formation from arachidonic acid, and also why only prostaglandins with a cis relationship between the C-9 and C-11 hydroxyls are found in nature.

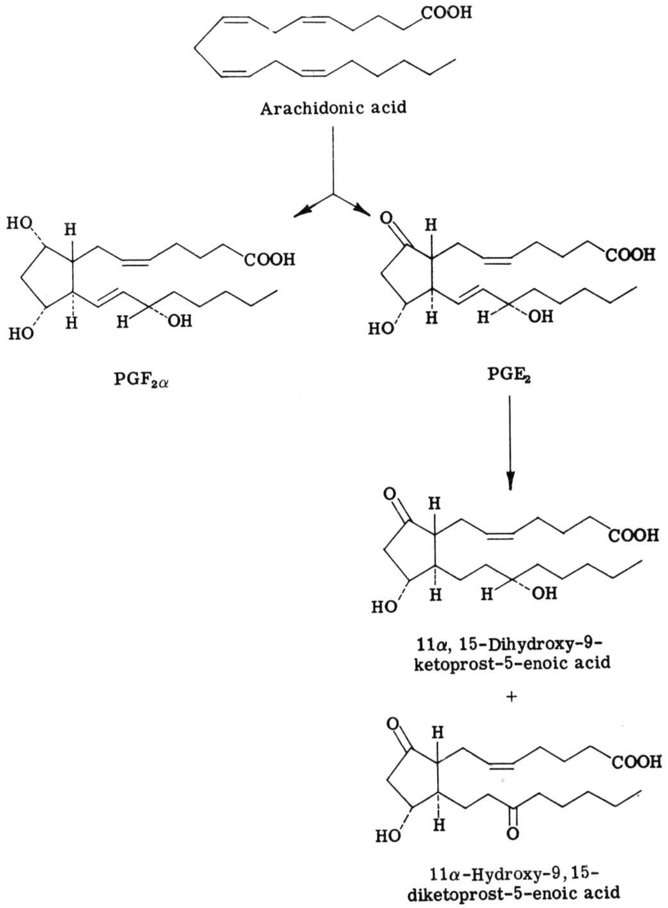

FIG. 2.12. Formation of prostaglandins from arachidonic acid in guinea pig lung (after Änggård and Samuelsson, 1965a).

Various observations in connection with the biosynthesis indicated that the conversion takes place in a few steps or possibly in one concerted reaction. The reaction appears to start with removal of hydrogen from carbon atom 13, isomerization of the

11-cis double bond to 12-trans with attachment of an oxygen molecule at position 11. A second phase in the conversion may be attachment of O_2 at position 15 with ring closure between carbons 8 and 12 and formation of a peroxy bridge between carbons 9 and 11 or attack of the peroxy radical at carbon 9, ring closure and O_2 capture at carbon 15. The reaction terminates by rearrangement of the (unstable) cyclic peroxide and reduction of the peroxy radical at carbon 15. In the presence of glutathione, the endo peroxide is split when forming the 11-hydroxy-9-oxocyclopentane derivative, which results in a high yield of PGE_1. The reaction can be represented in the following way:

$$C_{20}H_{34}O_2 + 2O_2 + 2GSH \rightarrow C_{20}H_{34}O_5 + GSSG + H_2O$$

The lipoxidase catalyzed introduction of oxygen into poly-unsaturated fatty acids possesses a high degree of specificity, as shown by Hamberg and Samuelsson (1965b).

The PGE formed during biosynthesis can be determined by measuring the increase in absorption at 278 nm after alkali treatment. The PGE_1 and other products could be determined by thin-layer chromatography.

The enzymic activity in various sheep organs converting dihomo-γ-linolenic acid into PGE_1 is given in Table 2.II.

In addition to PGE_1, dihomo-γ-linolenic acid yields small amounts of $PGF_{1\alpha}$ (Kupiecki, 1965) and also a less polar compound in larger amounts with sheep vesicular glands (Daniels et al., 1965). This compound proved on analysis to be PGE_1-217 (PGA_1). The authors did not exclude the possibility that at least part of the compound is formed by a nonenzymic process. With respect to its biological properties, it appeared noteworthy that the vasodepressor activity was relatively high in comparison with its smooth muscle stimulating effect, in contrast to PGE_1 and PGF_1. It may be recalled that extracts of the seminal vesicles of the monkey (vesiglandin) exert an effect of this kind (von Euler, 1935b, 1936).

The conversion of arachidonic acid to PGE_2 has also been achieved by using acetone powder from the seminal vesicle of the bull (Wallach, 1965) in the course of experiments in which it was independently assumed, on structural considerations, that certain unsaturated fatty acids might act as precursors of the prostaglandins.

TABLE 2.II

CONVERSION OF 1-^{14}C-DIHOMO-γ-LINOLENIC ACID INTO PGE$_1$
BY PARTICULATE FRACTIONS OF SHEEP TISSUES
(GLUTATHIONE PRESENT)[a]

Organ	Protein (mg)	20:3 (μg)	Radioactivity (%)	
			PGE$_1$ fraction	PGE$_1$-278 fraction (PGB$_1$)
Intestines	40	100	2.60	1.91
Lung	35	50	1.85	0.67
Uterus	36	50	0.79	0.75
Thymus	39	50	0.55	0.52
Heart	36	50	0.14	0.09
Liver	50	50	0.23	0.06
Kidney	40	50	0.14	0.01
Pancreas	60	100	0.06	0.01

[a] After Nugteren *et al.*, 1966b.

Bioconversion could also be demonstrated with material of human origin. On incubation of human ampulla ductus deferentis, seminal vesicles, and prostate gland with dihomo-γ-linolenic acid a small yield was obtained with all three organs. The yield from ampulla ductus deferentis was about one-third that of the other two organs (van Dorp, 1966,a,b). Even with human endometrium in the presence of glutathione, small amounts of PGE were formed (van Dorp, 1966a,b). The presence of glutathione has been shown to suppress the formation of the PGF's, although it favors the conversion to PGE.

The biosynthesis of prostaglandin in pig eye iris has been described by van Dorp *et al.* (1967) who found that this organ was able to convert dihomo-γ-linolenic acid into prostaglandin, although the conversion in other parts of the pig eye were doubtful. The prostaglandin obtained was mainly PGE$_1$ and to some extent $PGF_{1\alpha}$. In their isolation experiments, Änggård and Samuelsson (1964b) found $PGF_{1\alpha}$. However, the lipids of pig eye iris contain only arachidonic acid and very little dihomo-γ-linolenic acid, from which it follows that during *in vivo* synthesis of prostaglandins predominantly PGF_2 and PGE_2 would be expected to be formed.

As observed by Schneider *et al.* (1966), the 9-keto-15-hydroxy-10,13-prostadienoic acid obtained during the isolation procedure using sheep seminal vesicle homogenates occurred as an artifact.

2. SUBSTRATE SPECIFICITY AND COFACTORS

Only those substrates that have at least three methylene-interrupted cis double bonds, of which again at least three are in the 6, 9, and 12 positions from the terminal methyl group, seem to serve as precursors for the biosynthesis of PGE.

With the use of a particulate fraction from a homogenate of sheep vesicular gland, good conversion results were obtained only with a chain length of 19, 20, or 21 carbon atoms. The maximal yield was 65–75% (van Dorp, 1966a,b), measured by the conversion by alkali to PGB_1 (PGE_1-278) (Fig. 2.13).

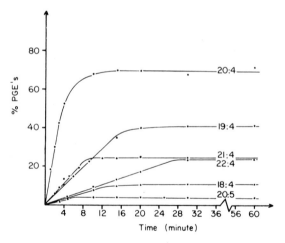

FIG. 2.13. Formation of PGE's from tetraenoic acids. Effect of chain length (after van Dorp, 1966a).

Polyunsaturated alcohols such as dihomo-γ-linoleyl alcohol and arachidonyl alcohol were not converted into prostanols (van Dorp, 1966a).

The bioconversion of unsaturated fatty acids to PGE's has been systematically studied by van Dorp and his group, who also synthetized all the substrates used. The tetraenoic fatty acids were converted into a series of PGE_2 homologs and the trienoic acid into PGE_1 homologs.

From these investigations it has emerged that the homologs of 20:4 ω 6[*] form a series of PGE_2 homologs, as is also the case with 20:3 ω 6. The only eicosatrienoic acid, apart from 20:3 ω 6, that shows a fairly high conversion into an iso-PGE_1 was 20:3 ω 7. A free carboxyl group is essential for the enzymic conversion of this kind (Struyk *et al.*, 1967). From the bioconversion experiments it followed that maximum conversion is obtained from the C_{20} fatty acids having the first double bond at the ω 6 position. Chain length seems to be less important to the yield than shifts in the double bond pattern.

The conditions for biosynthesis of PGE_1 from all-*cis*-8,11,14-eicosatrienoic acid (dihomo-γ-linolenic acid) have subsequently been studied in detail by Nugteren *et al.* (1966b). The enzymic material was a particulate fraction of sheep vesicular glands obtained by centrifugation at 100,000 g for 1 hour after removal of cell debris at lower speed from a homogenate of the gland with phosphate buffer, EDTA, and cysteine. The lyophilized sediment retained its activity for months when stored at −20°C. The enzymic material was incubated with the dihomo-γ-linolenic acid for 15 minutes at 30°C. It was found that the conversion was greatly enhanced in the presence of glutathione, which was much more active than cysteine or other SH-containing compounds. ATP or NADH had no stimulatory effect, but addition of an antioxidant such as hydroquinone proved useful. Cu^{2+} strongly inhibited the prostaglandin synthesis, although Fe^{2+} or Fe^{3+} had no effect. The reaction requires O_2, and, as found previously by

---

[*] The notation ω 6 indicates that the position of the first double bond is at carbon atom 6 counted from the terminal methyl group of the fatty acid.

Samuelsson (1965a), the oxygen atoms at positions 9 and 11 derive from the same oxygen molecule.

A number of by-products have been detected following the incubation of all-cis-8,11,14-eicosatrienoic acid, none of which could be converted enzymically to PGE$_1$. The main products are listed in the following tabulation with their R_f values on TLC with solvent system M I (Nugteren et al., 1966b) (Fig. 2.14).

	Product	R_f
I.	11-Hydroxy-8-cis,12-trans,14-cis-eicosatrienoic acid	0.50
II.	12-Hydroxy-8-trans,10-trans-heptadecadienoic acid	0.47
III.	11α-Hydroxy-9,15-dioxo-13-prostenoic acid	0.38
IV.	15-Hydroperoxy-11α-hydroxy-9-oxo-13-prostenoic acid (?)	0.25
V.	9α,15-Dihydroxy-11-oxo-13-prostenoic acid (iso-PGE$_1$) (?)	0.22
VI.	11α,15-Dihydroxy-9-oxo-13-prostenoic acid (PGE$_1$)	0.20
VII.	9α,11α,15-Trihydroxy-13-prostenoic acid (PGF$_{1α}$)	0.10

The conversion of dihomo-γ-linolenic acid to PGF$_{1α}$ by ovine and bovine seminal vesicle extracts has been reported by Kupiecki (1965).

Starting from borage seeds that contain a high percentage of γ-linolenic acid it was possible to scale up the enzymic conversion to dihomo-γ-linolenic acid (Pike et al., 1967). A series of prostaglandin analogs were prepared by chemical modification of natural material. Some of the PGF$_β$ compounds had noteworthy vasodepressor effects (cf. Chapter 4, Section C).

Total synthesis of dihydro-PGE$_1$ has recently been reported by Beal et al. (1966). 3-Ethoxy-2-cyclopentenone was used as the starting material. To this, by an elegant series of reactions, the proper side chains were added in order to form the ethyl ester of dihydro-PGE$_1$. The identity was proved by infrared spectra and other chemical means, as well as by biological assay (see also Beal et al., 1967).

Bogri et al. (1967) have reported on an improved synthesis and physicochemical evidence for the stereochemical assignments of ±11-deoxyprostaglandin F$_{1β}$.

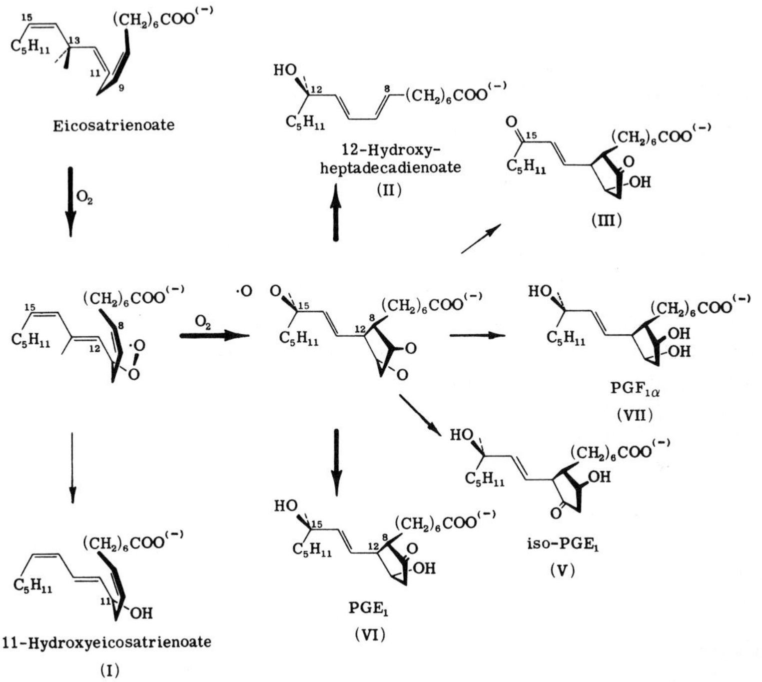

FIG. 2.14. Main by-products formed by incubation of all-*cis*-8,11,14-eicosa-trienoic acid with sheep vesicular gland enzymes (after Nugteren *et al.*, 1966b).

3. PREPARATIVE BIOSYNTHESIS

A method for the preparation of prostaglandins with example is given below, taken from the patent application no. 19,059 (Prov. B946).

"As precursors are used (18–22C) carboxylic acids or their derivatives of the general formula

$$\text{Me(CH}_2)_n(\text{CH}{=}\text{CH CH}_2)_p(\text{CH}_2)_q\text{CO}_2\text{M (II)}$$

where M = H, an alkali metal, or an alcohol residue; n = 0–7; p = 2–6; and q = 0–12.

"These are incubated with preparations of gonad, thymus, iris, lung, intestine, pancreas, adrenal, or brain tissue (III), at 10–60°C in buffer of pH 4–10 (pref. 7–9) with aeration, and with addition of salts, sugars (e.g., glucose), proteins (e.g., albumin), amino acids, vitamins, coenzymes, SH cofactors (e.g., glutathione), and antioxidants (e.g., propyl gallate), for 15–180 mins.

"Optimum results were obtained with II:III in ratio 1:1000 to 1:4000."

In the patent application, the following was given:

"Fresh sheep glandulae vesicalis (1.25 kg.) were ground with 0.1 M K-phosphate buffer (2.5 l.) of pH 7.5, and the slurry centrifuged 10 mins. at 2° and 4000 g. The supernatant liquor was removed, buffer (300 ml.) added to suspend the residue, recentrifuged and the liquors combined. The soln. contained 50 g. protein of which < 50 mg. was prostaglandin E (IV). This was incubated for 2 hrs. at 37°C, together with K-arachidonate (0.5 g.), 0.1 M K-phosphate buffer (2 l.) of pH 7.5, and cattle serum albumin (5 g.).

"96% EtOH (15 l.) was added, acidified to pH 4 (N-HCl), filtered and concd. to 1 l. in vac. below 30°C. Extracted (3 × 500 ml. Et₂O), dried evapd., and residue (15 g.) partitioned between 66% MeOH–Aq. (750 ml.) and petrol (750 ml.). Aqueous phase evapd. in vac., giving 3 g. residue containing 340 mg. IV. Dissolved in EtOAc:PhH (3:7) and chromat. on SiO₂ (activated at 115°C) in a 30 × 2 cm. column. Washed with 3:7-EtOAc:PhH, and eluted with 4:6-EtOAc:PhH, estimating IV by absorption at 278 mμ in 0.5 N NaOH in 50% EtOH–Aq. Fractions combined and purified in 1 g. portions on a silanised Hyflo-1:1 CHCl₃ isooctane column (22.5 g. packing and 20 ml. stationary phase). Yield 250 mg. pure IV."

4. TOTAL SYNTHESIS

The total synthesis of a pharmacologically active prostaglandin analog (11-deoxyprostaglandin-F₁α) was made by Bagli *et al.* (1966), and the first total synthesis of naturally occurring prostaglandins by Beal *et al.* (1966) came soon afterwards. The synthesis consists of the following four major steps, starting from cyclopentene-1,3-dione: (1) a modified Wittig reaction to introduce a C_7 side chain on the ring; (2) catalytic reduction of the chain; (3) a releated Wittig reaction for attachment of a C_8 chain; (4) catalytic reduction of the chain and the ring.

D. Distribution and Metabolism

With the aid of tritium-labeled PGE_1 prepared by Samuelsson (1964a), it became possible to study the metabolic fate of PGE_1 in the rat. In the 20 hours following its administration, about 50% of the radioactivity was recovered in urine and 10% in feces. High concentrations of tritium were found in the kidneys and in the liver, though the concentrations found in the lungs, adrenals, ovaries, uterus, and the pituitary gland were only slightly above the plasma level. In experiments on sheep, fairly high concentrations were found in the vesicular gland and the ampulla of the vas deferens and also in the fallopian tubes, uterus, and ovaries (Samuelsson, 1965b).

Studies with labeled PGE_1 in the rat showed that PGE_1 is completely metabolized to more polar derivatives, which is also the case in man (Samuelsson, 1965b).

Experiments on lung tissue have shown (Änggård and Samuelsson, 1964a, 1965b) that PGE_1 is converted to $11\alpha,15$-dihydroxy-9-ketoprostanoic acid (dihydro-PGE_1) and 11α-hydroxy-9,15-diketoprostanoic acid (15-ketodihydro-PGE_1), which involved reduction of the Δ^{13} double bond and, in the latter case, oxidation of the secondary alcohol group at C-15 (Fig. 2.15). The active enzymes are present in the nonparticulate fraction of the lung homogenate of various species including man and sheep. The same transformations also occur in other organs such as the small intestine and the kidneys. Since these metabolites are not found in rat urine, it appears that they are further metabolized before being excreted. PGE_2 and PGE_3 are metabolized in principally the same way.

$PGF_{1\alpha}$ was metabolized to a considerable degree to 2,3,-dinor-$PGF_{1\alpha}$ (Granström *et al.*, 1965).

The metabolism of PGE_2 was studied with the tritiated compound, prepared by selective catalytic reduction of the Δ^{17} double bond of PGE_3. When the labeled compound was incubated with a homogenate of guinea pig lung it was completely converted into two less polar metabolites. One of them was identified as $11\alpha,15$-dihydroxy-9-ketoprost-5-enoic acid, which had also been obtained during biosynthesis of PGE_2 from arachidonic acid with guinea pig lung. The second metabolite was also saturated at C-13 as shown by absence of ultraviolet absorption at 278 mμ after alkali treatment. On catalytic hydrogenation it yielded 15-ketodihydro-PGE_1 (Fig. 2.15) and was itself identified with 11α-hydroxy-9,15-diketoprost-5-enoic acid.

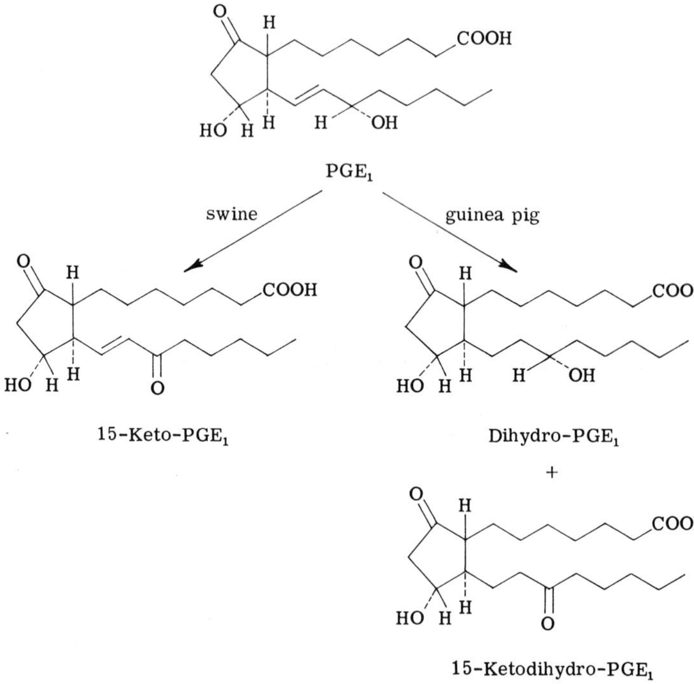

FIG. 2.15. Metabolism of PGE_1 in swine lung and guinea pig lung (after Änggård, 1966a, p. 16).

Incubation of labeled PGE$_3$, prepared from 5,8,11,14,17-eicosapentaenoic acid-^{14}C, with the soluble fraction of guinea pig-lung homogenate also caused conversion to two metabolites that were identified as 11α,15-dihydroxy-9-ketoprosta-5,17-dienoic acid and 11α-hydroxy-9,15-diketoprosta-5,17-dienoic acid (Änggård and Samuelsson, 1965b).

From the foregoing it can be seen that all three prostaglandins (PGE$_1$, PGE$_2$, and PGE$_3$) are metabolized in the same way, involving reduction of the Δ^{13} double bond and oxidation of the secondary alcohol group at C-15. The reduction of the Δ^{13} double bond was accompanied by loss of infrared absorption at 10.3 μ (trans double bond) which provided the information that the remaining double bonds were cis.

In swine lung, PGE$_1$ was converted to 15-keto-PGE$_1$ without concomitant reduction of the double bond (Änggård and Samuelsson, 1966). The oxidizing enzyme, 15-hydroxyprostaglandin dehydrogenase, was prepared and shown to specifically oxidize the hydroxyl group at C-15. NAD$^+$ was active as cofactor, but not NADP$^+$.

The distribution of ^{3}H-labeled PGE$_1$ in mice has been studied by means of autoradiography by Hansson and Samuelsson (1965). On intravenous injection the autoradiography of sagittal sections showed high concentrations of ^{3}H in the kidney, liver, and connective tissue. Lower but significant uptakes were also noted in the lungs and in the myometrium of the uterus.

3/Occurrence

New chemical methods for identification of the various prostaglandins have effectively contributed to the study of the occurrence of prostaglandins in various tissues. Some of the more pertinent data have been included in Table 3.I.

When prostaglandins occur in nanogram quantities, special precautions must be taken in order to avoid potential errors in isolation and identification. Various measures to avoid this effect have been proposed by Crowshaw (1966).

A. Human Seminal Plasma

1. TOTAL PROSTAGLANDIN ACTIVITY

Human seminal plasma contains factors with strong pharmacodynamic activity (Kurzrok and Lieb, 1930; Goldblatt, 1933, 1935; von Euler, 1934, 1935a, 1936; Cockrill *et al.*, 1935). This activity owes mainly or entirely to the occurrence of prostaglandins. The *total* activity—usually assayed on isolated organs such as rabbit jejunum—varies greatly between samples from different subjects ranging from a few "units" up to 60–80 (–100) "units"/ml (Asplund, 1947a; Eliasson, 1959; Hawkins and Labrum, 1961). In a more recent study, Horton and Thompson (1964) estimated the prostaglandin activity in several specimens of pooled human semen. The biological activity was assayed on isolated rabbit jejunum and isolated hamster colon and compared with pure PGE_1 activity. The mean concentration of prostaglandin corresponded to 226 μg of PGE_1 equivalents/ml (range,

41

TABLE 3.I

OCCURRENCE OF THE PROSTAGLANDINS

Tissue	Prostaglandin					Remarks	References
	E_1	E_2	E_3	$F_{1\alpha}$	$F_{2\alpha}$	$F_{3\alpha}$		
Human seminal plasma	x	x	x	x	x		In addition, 8 other PG's. Total smooth muscle-stimulating activity 100–600 PGE₁-Eq/ml (isolated rabbit jejunum)	Bergström and Samuelsson, 1962; Samuelsson, 1963a,b; Hamberg and Samuelsson, 1965, 1966; Bygdeman and Samuelsson, 1964, 1966, 1967
Human lung					x		0.02 μg/gm	Änggård, 1964, 1965
Human endometrium		x			x			Eglinton et al., 1963; Pickles et al., 1965
Monkey lung					x		0.2 μg/gm	Änggård, 1965
Pig lung					x			Bergström et al., 1962d
Sheep seminal plasma	x	x	x	x	x			Bergström et al., 1960; Horton and Thompson, 1964; Bygdeman and Holmberg, 1967

						Notes	References
Sheep vesicular glands	x	x	x	x			Bergström and Sjövall, 1960a,b; Bergström et al., 1962c
Sheep lung		x		x	x	x	0.5 μg PGF$_{2\alpha}$/gm; 0.04 μg PGE$_2$/gm	Bergström et al., 1962d; Ånggård and Samuelsson, 1963; Ånggård, 1965; Ånggård and Samuelsson, 1964b
Sheep iris				x				Samuelsson, 1964c
Bovine lung				x	x			Samuelsson, 1964b; Coceani and Wolfe, 1965; Wolfe et al., 1967
Bovine brain				x			0.3 μg/gm	
Cat thymus	x						0.8 μg/gm	Bergström and Samuelsson, 1963
Cat adrenal gland		(x)					Identity not fully established	Ramwell et al., 1966
Cat central nervous system				x				Ramwell and Shaw, 1963a,b; Ramwell, 1965; Wolfe et al., 1965, 1967; Horton and Main, 1966b
Rabbit renal medulla		x					In addition to PGA$_1$	Lee, 1967; Muirhead et al., 1967
Fowl central nervous system		x		x				Horton and Main, 1966b
Frog intestine	(x)		(x)				Identity not fully established	Suzuki and Vogt, 1965
Frog spinal cord		(x)						Ramwell, 1966

24–783). For comparison, the authors converted the results of previous workers into the same equivalents. The results are presented in Tables 3.II and 3.III.

TABLE 3.II
CONCENTRATION OF PROSTAGLANDIN IN 14 POOLED SAMPLES
OF HUMAN SEMEN[a,b]

Volume of semen (ml)	Weight of residue extracted by ether (mg)	Prostaglandin E_1 equivalent (μg/ml of semen)		
		Rabbit jejunum	Hamster colon	Mean
4.0	18	320, 212	471, 529	383
13.5	270	796, 844	746	783
49.4	134	111, 109	111, 109	110
52.0	98	32, 41	16, 21	27
3	33	313, 104	835, 42	324
33.0	183	11, 21	21, 42	24
13.0	240	47, 30	47, 26	37
10.0	275	88, 70	88, 70	79
24.0	195	466, 391	466, 520	461
2.6	32	133, 190	133, 190	162
2.0	322	164, 261	164, 164	188
49.0	847	192, 240	480, 360	318
29.0	204	111, 74	37, 37	65
7.0	91	204, 382	115, 130	208
Total means		213	240	226

[a] All samples were run on two thin-layer chromatograms and the zones corresponding to the position of prostaglandin E_1 were eluted and assayed using prostaglandin E_1 as standard. The four results so obtained and the means are given.
[b] After Horton and Thompson (1964).

Semen from men attending infertility clinics seems to contain on an average less prostaglandin activity than semen from fertile men (Asplund, 1947a; Eliasson, 1959; Hawkins and Labrum, 1961; Bygdeman and Samuelsson, 1966). In order to clarify this point, one needs, however, much more data from fertile men in the same age groups that usually attend the infertility clinics. Moreover, it is necessary to have relevant data about the overall cytology and biochemistry of the semen samples before any conclusions about the significance of a low prostaglandin activity in relation to male fertility can be made.

TABLE 3.III

COMPARISON OF THE ESTIMATED CONCENTRATIONS OF PROSTAGLANDIN IN HUMAN SEMEN REPORTED BY FOUR GROUPS OF INVESTIGATORS[a,b]

Reference	Approximate PGE_1 equivalent of 1 unit $(\mu g/U)$	PGE_1 equivalent $(\mu g/ml$ of semen)		No. of samples	Origin of samples
		Mean	Range		
Asplund (1947)	4.5	37	<20–90	155	Individual ejaculates from fertility clinics
Eliasson (1959)	6.75	81	10–203	16	Individual ejaculates from 16 infertile patients
		187	74–405	13	Individual ejaculates from 3 healthy subjects
Hawkins and Labrum (1961)	20	122	34–448	50	Individual ejaculates from fertility clinics
Present investigation	–	226	24–783	14	Pooled samples from fertility clinics

[a] The results of previous workers have been converted to prostaglandin E_1 equivalents ($\mu g/ml$ of semen) using the conversion factor shown in the second column.

[b] After Horton and Thompson (1964).

2. PROSTAGLANDINS E AND F

The smooth muscle-stimulating activity in human semen owes to a number of prostaglandin compounds. Samuelsson (1963a,b) demonstrated the presence of PGE_1, PGE_2, PGE_3, $PGF_{1\alpha}$, and $PGF_{2\alpha}$. Recently, a chemical method has been described (Bygdeman and Samuelsson, 1964, 1966) that allows the quantitative determination of these prostaglandins in single samples of semen. Tritium-labeled PGE_1 and $PGF_{1\alpha}$ were added to the sample in order to determine the recovery of the PGE and PGF compounds and for identification purposes. The mean recovery of labeled PGE$_1$ was about 70% and in repetitive determinations with samples from a pool of human semen the method proved its accuracy. The results from the assay of several separate samples

TABLE 3.IV

DETERMINATION OF PROSTAGLANDINS (μg/ml) IN HUMAN SEMEN OBTAINED FROM MEN WITH NORMAL FERTILITY[a]

Subject	PGE$_1$	PGE$_2$	PGE$_3$	PGF$_{1\alpha}$	PGF$_{2\alpha}$
1	24	17	5.7	2.2	1.2
2	19	15	4.5	3.7	4.2
3	24	24	7.6	3.0	5.1
4	30	30	4.0	6.8	7.3
5	30	27	7.8	3.5	4.5
6	20	25	3.5	2.4	3.9
Mean value	25	23	5.5	3.6	4.4

[a] After Bygdeman and Samuelsson (1966).

TABLE 3.V

DETERMINATION OF PROSTAGLANDINS (μg/ml) IN HUMAN SEMEN OBTAINED FROM MEN SUBMITTING SAMPLES AT FERTILITY LABORATORIES[a]

Sample No.	PGE$_1$	PGE$_2$	PGE$_3$	PGF$_{1\alpha}$	PGF$_{2\alpha}$	Spermatozoa ($\times 10^{-6}$/ml)	Abnormal cells (%)	Motility grading[b]
1	31.5	9.8	2.2	1.7	0.6	87	48.5	3–2
2	20.7	9.7	2.5	1.5	0.6	42.5	78	2–1
3	27.0	21.8	4.5	3.5	2.0	7.2	84.5	1
4	27.0	16.0	5.1	2.4	1.2	144	25.5	3–2
5	33.9	6.7	10.5	2.5	1.2	153	23.5	2–1
6	26.1	21.4	2.6	2.6	1.6	113	50.5	3–2
7	32.1	34.1	2.4	—[c]	—[c]	82	52	3–2
8	5.7	7.0	0	—[c]	—[c]	216	53.5	0
9	24.0	21.5	1.4	2.8	3.2	50.5	49.5	3–2
10	1.9	2.3	0	<0.05	<0.05	48.4	66.5	3–2

[a] After Bygdeman and Samuelsson (1966).
[b] 3 = very good motility; 2 = good motility; 1 = slight motility; 0 = no motility.
[c] Not analyzed.

from men with normal fertility are presented in Table 3.IV and those from men in childless marriages in Table 3.V. In accordance with previous studies, some semen specimens from men in childless marriages had low prostaglandin content.

3. PROSTAGLANDINS A AND B

It should be noted that the figures presented in Tables 3.IV and 3.V are low compared to the total biological activity of semen (cf. Tables 3.II and 3.III). This difference is, however, explained by the observation that human semen contains eight additional prostaglandins all with smooth muscle-stimulating activity (Hamberg and Samuelsson, 1965a, 1966, 1967). Four of these, PGA_1 (PGE_1-217), PGA_2, PGB_1 (PGE_1-278), and PGB_2, were known earlier since they were found by treating PGE_1 and PGE_2 with NaOH to give chromophores with absorption maxima at 217 and 278 nm (Bergström *et al.*, 1963a). These compounds had, however, not been isolated earlier from natural sources. The other four prostaglandins had the same parent structure and an additional hydroxyl group at C-19 (Fig. 2.4). The total amount of PGA_1, PGA_2, PGB_1, and PGB_2 in semen is about the same as that for PGE_1, PGE_2, and PGE_3, though the 19-hydroxylated compounds occur in concentrations about four times as high.

It is not known to what extent the various prostaglandin compounds influence the biological action of each other, and comparative biological and chemical assay procedures are, therefore, needed.

4. RELATION TO OTHER SEMEN PROPERTIES

Hawkins and Labrum (1956, 1961) reported a correlation between the prostaglandin content and the maintenance of the spermatozoal activity. Such a correlation was, however, not obtained by Asplund (1947a) or by Eliasson and Olsson (reported in Eliasson, 1959). No correlation has been found between prostaglandin activity and the number or morphology of the spermatozoa (Asplund, 1947a; Eliasson, 1959; Hawkins and Labrum, 1961; Bygdeman and Samuelsson, 1966), nor between total prostaglandin activity tested on isolated rabbit jejunum and the concentration of fructose and cholesterol, or the acid phosphatase and aspartate aminotransferase activities (Eliasson, unpublished). Marked variations in the total prostaglandin activity are sometimes found in semen samples from the same individual, which is in contrast to the relatively constant pattern of some other biochemical factors in the seminal plasma from healthy young men (Eliasson, 1959, 1965).

In a recent study, Bygdeman and Eliasson (to be published) found no correlation between the concentrations of PGE_1 and fructose in the seminal plasma. Specimens with normal fructose levels could be almost devoid of PGE_1 and vice versa. This seems of principal interest since fructose and prostaglandin are both secreted from the seminal vesicles. Moreover, fructose is regarded a good indicator of the androgen production from the testis.

According to von Euler (1936) and Eliasson (1959), the smooth muscle-stimulating properties of human semen owe almost entirely to its content of prostaglandins. Vandelli (1943) claims, however, the presence of about 2 μg of histamine/ml (range, 0–15 μg/ml). There is no chemical evidence for the occurrence of acetylcholine (Mann, 1964) or 5-hydroxytryptamine (Eliasson, 1961; Mann et al., 1961).

The presence in extracts of human seman of an oxytocic principle that could be partially destroyed by aminopeptidase has been claimed by Hawker et al. (1960).

5. ORIGIN

In order to study the origin of human seminal prostaglandins, Eliasson (1959) used the "split-ejaculation" method developed by Lundquist (1949). The ejaculate is collected in a tray with boxes in such a way that the first portion is caught in box No. 1, the second in box No. 2, etc. Each box is then analyzed for components specific to each of the main glands contributing to the production of semen, i.e., acid phosphatase from the prostate gland, fructose from the seminal vesicles, and spermatozoa from the testes, epididymis, and vas deferens. The results from a typical experiment are presented in Fig. 3.1 and illustrate that prostaglandin originates from the same organ as fructose, i.e., the seminal vesicles.

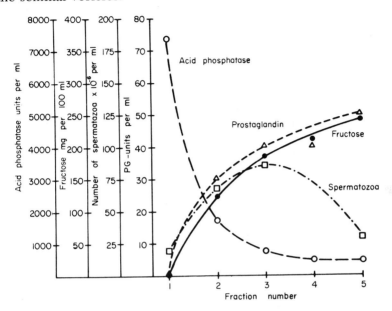

FIG. 3.1. Distribution of acid phosphatase, total prostaglandin, fructose, and spermatozoa in a "split-ejaculation" from a healthy man. Note the similarity in distribution for prostaglandins and fructose, indicating that they have the same origin, i.e., the seminal vesicles (after Eliasson, 1963).

B. Seminal Fluid from Other Species

Sheep and goat seminal fluid was shown to have smooth muscle-stimulating activity owing most likely to prostaglandins (von Euler, 1936; Eliasson, 1959). The activity corresponded to about 5–55 units/ml. Horton and Thompson (1964) found the activity in ram semen "collected out of season by electro-ejaculation" to be 7.3 μg of PGE$_1$-equivalent/ml (the relation-ship between the units given above and PGE$_1$ is about 6–7 μg of PGE$_1$/unit).

Bergström *et al.* (1960) isolated PGE$_1$ from sheep semen and also found at least one other prostaglandin-like compound to be present. Quantitative determination of the various prostaglandins in pooled sheep seminal fluid was later carried out by Bygdeman and Holmberg (1966). The results were 28 μg of PGE$_1$, 3.2 μg of PGE$_2$, 2.0 μg of PGE$_3$, 5 μg of PGF$_{1\alpha}$, and 2.3 μg of PGF$_{2\alpha}$ per milliliter of semen. The 19-hydroxylated prostaglandins present in human semen could not be detected in ram semen.

Seminal fluid from horse, ox, dog, and rabbit contains no prostaglandins (or very small amounts, less than 0.5 μg of PGE$_1$-equivalent/ml) (von Euler, 1936; Eliasson, 1959; Horton and Thompson, 1964).

Monkey semen *(Macacus rhesus)* contains a blood pressure-lowering factor, probably chemically related to the prostaglandins, that in biological tests can be separated from the prostaglandin extracts prepared from human semen. The factor has been named vesiglandin (see Chapter 5,A) (von Euler, 1935b, 1936). It appears to have some properties similar to PGA$_1$ (PGE$_1$-217).

C. Male Accessory Genital Organs

Sheep vesicular glands and ampullae ductus deferentis contain appreciable amounts of prostaglandins (von Euler, 1934; 1936; Eliasson, 1959). From these glands Bergström *et al.* isolated PGE$_1$, PGE$_2$, PGE$_3$, and PGF$_{1\alpha}$ (Bergström and Sjövall, 1960a,b; Bergström *et al.*, 1962c).

The total activity extracted from the vesicular glands corresponds to about 2.5 units per gram of tissue if an acid medium is used for the extraction (von Euler, 1939; Eliasson, 1959), but a much higher yield can be obtained if the extraction is performed at a pH around 7.5; the maximum amounts are of the order of 60–80 units/gm (Eliasson, 1958a, 1959).

The results indicated that the active prostaglandins were either bound in the tissue in an inactive form such that the activity was released by an enzymic process, or formed from an inactive precursor. Recent studies by Bergström *et al.* (1964a) and van Dorp *et al.* (1964a) have shown that the sheep vesicular glands contain enzymes capable of transforming certain essential fatty acids into prostaglandins, e.g., arachidonic acid to PGE_2. This is further discussed in Chapter 2,C.

Prostaglandin activity has not been found in extracts from the following organs: prostate and bulbo-urethral glands of sheep, and male accessory genital glands of ox, pig, dog, cat, rabbit, guinea pig, hamster, rat, and mouse (von Euler, 1934: Eliasson, 1959; Horton and Thompson, 1964).

Extracts from the prostate and vesicular glands of *Macacus rhesus* contain vesiglandin activity (von Euler, 1935b, 1939) (see Chapter 5,A).

D. Ovary, Endometrium, Menstrual Fluid, and Umbilical Cord

It was reported by von Euler and Hammarström (1937) that ovarial extracts from cows and sows contained biological activity of a kind similar to that of prostaglandin. The active principle could be extracted with aqueous alkali from an acidic ethereal solution and behaved in this medium as an organic acid. The activity in cow and sow ovarial extracts when tested on the rabbit blood pressure and rabbit jejunum corresponded to approximately 0.1 units/gm of fresh tissue or about a thirtieth of the activity of the vesicular gland of sheep. After the intravenous injection of ^{3}H-labeled PGE_1 in sheep, Samuelsson (1965b) found the same high recovery of activity in the ovary as in the uterus.

Smooth muscle-stimulating lipids have been isolated from human endometrium and menstrual fluid (Pickles, 1957; Chambers and Pickles, 1958). The active factors were separated into the three components, A, B, and C, in decreasing order of polarity (Clitheroe, 1961, Clitheroe and Pickles, 1961). Component A was later shown to contain several active substances; the main ones were referred to as A_1 and A_2 (Pickles and Hall, 1963). These two components have now been identified as $PGF_{2\alpha}$ (A_1) and PGE_2 (A_2) (Eglinton *et al.*, 1963). These two prostaglandins account for the major part of the activity in menstrual fluid.

The total prostaglandin recovery from endometrial curettings was approximately 35 ng/gm net weight of tissue for the proliferatory phase, and about 50 ng/gm for the secretory phase. The

PGF:PGE ratio was most likely higher in the secretory than in the proliferatory phase (Pickles *et al.*, 1965). The authors, however, regard these figures as the lower limit rather than as the probably true values for the original tissue.

The average amount of $PGF_{2\alpha}$ collected during a menstruation was about 5 μg and the amount of PGE_2 about 0.1 μg. Provided that all the prostaglandin activity originates from the endometrium (about 5 gm), this would give a production of approximately 1 μg/gm tissue (Pickles *et al.*, 1965). It is known that seminal prostaglandins are absorbed in the vagina (Asplund, 1947b; Eliasson and Posse, 1960, 1965; Horton *et al.*, 1963; Sandberg *et al.*, 1967); they are probably also taken up by the blood vessels in the uterus. Therefore, it appears likely that the prostaglandin production by the endometrium is still higher.

In one young girl, the "menstrual stimulant" activity was studied in 19 of her first 23 periods. The activity of the postanovular periods averaged 16% of that of the post-ovular periods ($p = < 0.01$), indicating control by corpus luteum (Pickles, 1966).

The presence of prostaglandins E_1, E_2, $F_{1\alpha}$, and $F_{2\alpha}$ in amniotic fluid and in the umbilical cord vessels has been reported by Karim (1967). Their possible function in closure of the umbilical blood vessels, previously observed in the perfused human placenta by von Euler (1938), is discussed.

E. Lung Tissue

Lipid extracts of lung tissue contain smooth muscle-stimulating factors (Eliasson, 1959; Linn *et al.*, 1961). Bergström *et al.* (1962d) first isolated $PGF_{2\alpha}$ from sheep and pig lungs. The same prostaglandin was also isolated from the lungs of man, monkey, and guinea pig (Änggård and Samuelsson, 1963; Änggård, 1964, 1965). Silicic acid chromatography of a lipid extract from guinea pig lung reveals at least four peaks with smooth muscle-stimulating activity, one of which owes to $PGF_{2\alpha}$ (Fig. 3.2) (Änggård, 1965). The approximate concentrations of $PGF_{2\alpha}$ in lungs from different species are given in Table 3.VI. Postmortem degradation cannot be excluded as a contributing cause to the low prostaglandin concentration in human lung tissue.

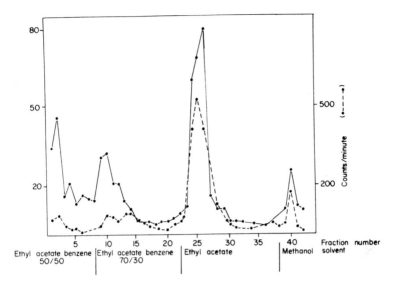

FIG. 3.2. Silicic acid chromatography of smooth muscle-stimulating material from an extract (1.93 gm) of guinea pig lung. The radioactivity owes to tritium-labeled $PGF_{2\alpha}$ added at the beginning of the extraction. The smooth muscle-stimulating activity (●) was tested on the isolated rabbit jejunum against a standard of $PGF_{2\alpha}$. Column, 100 gm; fraction volume, 250 ml (after Änggård, 1965).

TABLE 3.VI

APPROXIMATE CONCENTRATIONS OF $PGF_{2\alpha}$ ($\mu g/g$) IN LUNGS
FROM DIFFERENT SPECIES[a]

Species	$PGF_{2\alpha}$	Remarks
Sheep	0.5	Fresh
Guinea pig	0.5	Fresh
Macacus rhesus	0.2	Obtained 2–3 hours after death
Human	0.02	Obtained 7–24 hours after death

[a] After Änggård (1965).

In addition to $PGF_{2\alpha}$, it has been demonstrated that bovine lung contains $PGF_{3\alpha}$ (Samuelsson, 1964c) and that sheep lung contains small amounts of $PGF_{1\alpha}$, $PGF_{3\alpha}$, and PGE_2 (Änggård, 1965).

An interesting observation is that lung tissue from some animals has enzymes capable of transforming essential fatty acids into prostaglandins (Änggård and Samuelsson, 1965a; van Dorp, 1966b; see also Chapter 2, Sections C and D).

A review of work on prostaglandins in the lung has been published by Änggård (1966a).

F. Iris

The irides from rabbit, cat, dog, sheep, ox, and man contain smooth muscle-stimulating activity and have chemical and biological properties similar to the prostaglandins (Ambache, 1957a,b, 1959, 1966; Ambache et al., 1966a; Änggård and Samuelsson, 1964b). The active principle has been named irin (Ambache, 1957a).

By chromatography on silica gel of the acetone- and ether-purified extract from sheep iris, Änggård and Samuelsson (1964b) eluted several peaks (Fig. 3.3). The active compound in

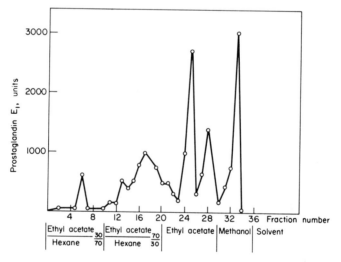

FIG. 3.3. Silicic acid chromatography of a lipid extract from sheep iris. The smooth muscle-stimulating activity was assayed on rabbit duodenum. One prostaglandin E_1 unit was equivalent to the effect produced by 1 μg of prostaglandin E_1 (after Änggård and Samuelsson, 1964b).

one of these (fraction No. 24–29) was identified as $PGF_{2\alpha}$. Part of the activity in rabbit and cat irin preparations owes to $PGF_{2\alpha}$ and PGE_2 (Ambache *et al.*, 1966b).

The irin activity is markedly different in various species. The sheep and ox iris contain, for example, only 10% of the activity in rabbit and dog iris (Ambache, 1959; Ambache *et al.*, 1966a).

Recently, van Dorp *et al.* (1967) have succeeded in demonstrating the biosynthesis of PGE_1 with enzymes from pig iris using dihomo-γ-linolenic acid as substrate (cf. Chapter 2, Section C,1).

G. Nervous System

1. CENTRAL NERVOUS SYSTEM

Brain tissue from horse, dog, cat, rabbit, rat, and guinea pig contains smooth muscle-stimulating lipid acids (Ambache and Reynolds, 1960; Ambache *et al.*, 1963; Kirschner and Vogt, 1961; Toh, 1963; Wolfe *et al.*, 1965). Part of this activity most likely owes to prostaglandins.

Prostaglandin $F_{2\alpha}$ was first isolated from bovine brain by Samuelsson (1964b), who estimated the amount to about 0.3 μg/gm wet weight. The presence of prostaglandin $F_{2\alpha}$ in brains from ox, cat, rabbit, and fowl has also been claimed by Coceani and Wolfe (1965), Wolfe *et al.* (1967), Horton and Main (1966b), and Ambache *et al.* (1966b). Prostaglandin E_2 appears to be present in brain and spinal cord of the rabbit and fowl (Horton and Main, 1966b; Ambache *et al.*, 1966b).

The distribution of prostaglandins in the central nervous system of the dog has been studied in more detail by Holmes and Horton (1967). Prostaglandins were extracted according to Horton and Main (1966b), separated chromatographically and estimated biologically. In Table 3.VII, the amounts of prostaglandins E and F are given in various parts of the dog brain.

From the table it can be seen that prostaglandins E and F occur in all parts of the dog brain examined. As remarked by the authors, the even distribution (except in medulla and white matter) suggests some other function than that of a transmitter.

Homogenization of the brain tissue in buffer salt solution (pH

7.4) and incubation for 1 hour increase the yield of prostaglandin about 10 times compared to control experiments. The increase in activity seems to owe mainly to the formation of $PGF_{2\alpha}$ (Wolfe et al., 1967).

TABLE 3.VII

DISTRIBUTION OF PROSTAGLANDINS IN THE CENTRAL NERVOUS SYSTEM OF THE DOG[a]

Area	Prostaglandins E	Prostaglandins F
Cortex	86 (13) 20.5–185	147 (13) 58–389
Hippocampi	62 (3) 19–140	195 (3) 180–214
Caudate nuclei	72 (2) 34–109	149 (2) 143–154
Hypothalamus	60 (3) 24–109	200 (3) 154–240
Cerebellum	107 (2) 75–138	144 (2) 107–180
Medulla	21 (3) 2.5–39	130 (3) 80–178
Spinal cord	104 (3) 65–168	191 (3) 56–416
White matter	27 (1)	106 (1)
Cortex (from dog anaes- thetized with bromethol)	184 (1)	204 (1)

[a] Total prostaglandins E expressed in terms of E_1 and total prostaglandins F in terms of $F_{1\alpha}$. All values are uncorrected for recovery and are expressed in terms of ng/gm of tissue. The number of estimations is given in parentheses followed by the ranges (Holmes and Horton, 1967).

2. RELEASE FOLLOWING NERVE AND DRUG STIMULATION

Prostaglandins or prostaglandin-like compounds have been reported to occur in superfusates of the cat brain (Ramwell and Shaw, 1963b, 1966; Coceani and Wolfe, 1965; Ramwell, 1965; Wolfe et al., 1965). The amount obtained in the superfusate corresponded to 0.4–0.9 ng of PGE_1-equivalents/15 minutes/cm^2 of surface (Wolfe et al., 1967). (The activity was determined on superfused rat stomach fundus.)

Recently, Feldberg and Myers (1966) have reported that the effluent from the anterior and inferior horn of the perfused cerebral ventricles in the anesthetized cat contains a lipid-soluble hydroxy acid apparently related to the prostaglandins. In the effluent from the inferior horn, the whole activity appeared to be caused by the prostaglandin-like principle. No consistent relationships were noted between the neuronal activity and the amount of prostaglandin-like substance in the effluent, except in one experiment in which hippocampal activation was elicited by tubocurarine and followed by a 5-fold increase in activity in the effluent.

Perfusates of frog spinal cord contained at least six smooth-muscle stimulating compounds including a polypeptide, serotonin, and prostaglandins. Chemical, chromatographic, and pharmacological tests indicated a mixture of PGE_1 and $PGE_{1\alpha}$. Bilateral stimulation of the frog hind limb elicits an increased release of the prostaglandins and acetylcholine. The addition of 5-hydroxytryptamine, dopa, or the monoamine oxidase inhibitor tranylcypromine to the perfusing fluid increased the amount of prostaglandins found in the perfusate (Shaw, 1965; Ramwell, 1966; Ramwell *et al.*, 1966b). On the basis of their findings, the authors suggest that the prostaglandin release is associated with the prior release of biogenic amines.

Ramwell *et al.* (1965) have reported that direct or indirect stimulation of the rat diaphragm caused a release of smooth muscle-stimulating substances (Fig. 3.4) that behave like a prostaglandin mixture during thin-layer chromatography. The muscle or the nerve was stimulated at 25 stimuli per second with a 0.03-msec pulse duration. On chromatography of the active principle, the major fraction, dissolved in ether, showed an R_f value corresponding to PGE_1. The amount of PGE_1 equivalents released on nerve stimulation amounted to about 1 ng/minute. Extraction of the whole homogenized diaphragm yielded approximately 125 ng of PGE_1-equivalents/gm of muscle. The presence of a blocking dose of *d*-tubocurarine in the bath did not prevent the release of prostaglandins. On the other hand, both adrenaline and noradrenaline (0.5–5 μg/ml of bath fluid) caused release of prostaglandins. Ramwell (personal communication) found that acetylcholine also released prostaglandins from the diaphragm.

Acidic lipids have also been found in the blood perfusing dog spleen upon stimulation of the splenic nerves (Davies *et al.*, 1967). From chromatographic and other studies it was concluded that some of the material released consisted of PGE_2. The splenic blood collected during stimulation contained PGE_2 in concentrations up to 200 ng/ml. The output of the active compound was blocked by phenoxybenzamine. It is not known whether the prostaglandins are released from the sympathetic nerves or from the smooth muscle of the spleen. Shaw (1966) has found that sympathetic nerve stimulation releases prostaglandins from the rat epididymal fat pad *in vitro*.

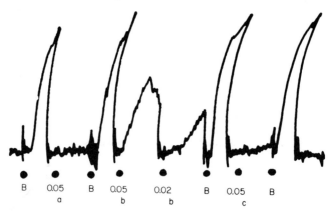

B   0.05   B   0.05   0.02   B   0.05   B
        a   b   b   c

FIG. 3.4. Recorder trace showing the isometric response of an isolated rat uterus. The uterus responded by contraction to 0.25 μg/ml of bradykinin (B) and to samples of an extract of the bath fluid collected during (0.05 and 0.02 ml, b) but not before (0.05 ml, a) or after (0.05 ml, c) stimulation of the phrenic nerve. The active material released on stimulation of the nerve sensitized the tissue to subsequent doses of bradykinin. The diaphragm bath fluid (1 ml) was acidified (pH 2) and extracted three times with ether (1:1 by volume); the extract was dried under reduced pressure at 30°C and reconstituted for testing in 0.5 ml of De Jalon solution (after Ramwell *et al.*, 1965).

It has been reported that prostaglandin $F_{1\alpha}$ appears in the venous effluent from the perfused adrenals of the cat when catecholamine secretion is induced by acetylcholine (Ramwell *et al.*, 1966a; Shaw and Ramwell, 1967). Possibly, acetylcholine activates a phospholipase A in the adrenal gland which splits off prostaglandin from membranes and thus allows catecholamines to escape. The possibility is also considered that prostaglandin formation is a common accompaniment of secretory activity.

H. Other Tissues

In a study of the prostaglandin content of various organs from sheep, von Euler and Hammarström (1937) found considerably less than 1 unit in extracts from 500 gm of brain, 100 gm of liver, 40 gm of pancreas, 30 gm of testicle, 20 gm of intestine, and 40 gm of skeletal muscle when tested on rabbit blood pressure. An effect corresponding to 1 unit on the rabbit jejunum was observed in 40 gm of pancreas, 20 gm of intestine, and 40 gm of skeletal muscle.

The calf thymus contains two smooth muscle-stimulating factors, one of which has been identified as PGE_1 (0.8 μg/gm). No PGF-compounds have been detected (Bergström and Samuelsson, 1963).

The human, rabbit, porciné, and bovine renal medullas contain smooth muscle-stimulating lipids with chemical and biological properties resembling those of prostaglandins. One of these compounds has been identified as PGA_1; another is most likely PGE_2 (Hickler *et al.*, 1964a,b; Lee *et al.*, 1965; Lee, 1967; Muirhead *et al.*, 1967; Strong *et al.*, 1966).

Spasmogenic unsaturated hydroxy acids have been demonstrated in frog intestine dialyzates, in longitudinal muscle sheets from rabbit and guinea pig intestines. Part of the biological activity apparently owes to prostaglandins (both E and F) Ambache *et al.*, 1966b; Suzuki and Vogt, 1965; Vogt *et al.*, 1967).

4/Biological Effects

A. Human Uterus

1. IN VITRO

a. Nonpregnant Myometrium

The normal response of isolated strips from nonpregnant human myometrium to human semen, to a total prostaglandin extract of this fluid (HSF-PG), or to the various PGE compounds is a decrease in the amplitude and frequency of the spontaneous contractions as illustrated in Figs. 4.1 and 4.2 (Kurzrok and Lieb, 1930; Cockrill et al., 1935; Eliasson, 1959; Bygdeman and Eliasson, 1963a,b; Eglinton et al., 1963; Pickles and Hall, 1963; Sandberg et al., 1963b, 1964; Bygdeman, 1964, 1967; Bygdeman et al., 1966; Bygdeman and Hamberg, 1967).

The human myometrium is very sensitive to prostaglandin E; the threshold doses for E_1, E_2, and E_3 are of the order of 0.01–0.1 µg/ml of bath fluid. The activity ratio for these three prostaglandins is about 1.0.8.0.7 (Bygdeman and Eliasson, 1963b). Human semen also contains four dehydrated prostaglandins, PGA_1 (PGE_1-217), PGB_1 (PGE_1-278), PGA_2, and PGB_2, and four 19-hydroxylated compounds (cf. Chapter 3 and Fig. 2.4). Their effect on the human myometrium is the same as that of the PGE's (Fig. 4.3), and the activity of these two groups in relation to PGE_1 is about 0.1–0.3 : 1 and 0.03–0.1 : 1, respectively (Bygdeman et al., 1966; Bygdeman and Samuelsson, 1967). These activity ratios and the known amounts of the various compounds in semen from

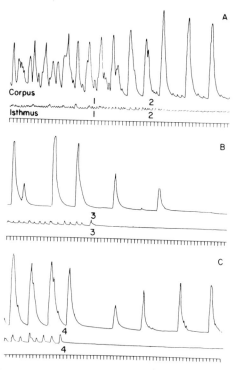

FIG. 4.1. Effect of native seminal fluid and semen prostaglandin extract on isolated strips from the corpus and the isthmus of human nonpregnant uterus in late proliferatory stage. Bath volume, 220 ml. Between records A, B, and C there were 30–60 minutes per interval. Time in minutes. Prostaglandin extracted from human seminal fluid: 1 = 0.5 unit, 2 = 1 unit, 3 = 2.5 units. Native human seminal fluid: 4 = 0.02 ml (after Eliasson, 1959).

fertile men correspond well with the biological activity of the native seminal plasma, i.e., on the isolated myometrium 0.1 μl of seminal fluid per milliliter of bath fluid gives a clear inhibition of the motility, as shown in Fig. 4.1.

In some instances, the response of the myometrium to HSF-PG and prostaglandins E is an increase in the amplitude of the contractions or in tonus, a phenomenon that is most commonly observed after the addition of very small amounts of prostaglandins. On addition of repeated doses or larger amounts, the

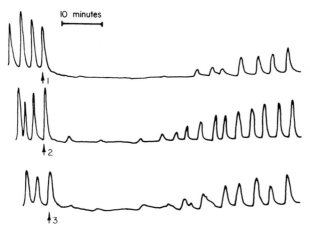

FIG. 4.2. The effect of PGE_1, PGE_2, and PGE_3 on isolated human myometrium. The strips are from an uterus in middle secretory phase: $1 = 0.03$ μg/ml of PGE_1; $2 = 0.03$ μg/ml of PGE_2; $3 = 0.03$ μg/ml of PGE_3 (after Bygdeman and Eliasson, 1963b).

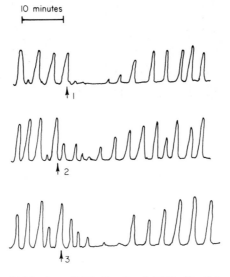

FIG. 4.3. Effect of 19-hydroxy-PGA_2 ($1 = 3$ μg), PGB_1 ($2 = 0.3$ μg), and PGE_1 ($3 = 0.1$ μg) on three isolated myometrial strips from a uterus in late proliferative phase. Bath volume, 40 ml (after Bygdeman *et al.*, 1966).

same muscle strips usually react with inhibition (Fig. 4.1). In some experiments, however, the stimulating effect persists. It was noted that myometrial strips with this reactivity pattern had been obtained from patients early or late in the menstrual period (Eliasson, 1959; Bygdeman and Eliasson, 1963a; Pickles and Hall, 1963).

Contrary to the behavior displayed by prostaglandins E, the F compounds stimulate the contraction of the isolated human myometrium. The actions of $F_{1\alpha}$ and $F_{2\alpha}$ are only weak on strips from nonpregnant myometrium taken at midcycle, but more marked on preparations from late in the menstrual cycle (Fig. 4.4) or from pregnant women (Bygdeman and Eliasson, 1963b; Pickles and Hall, 1963; Sandberg et al., 1965). $PGF_{1\beta}$ and $PGF_{2\beta}$ have a low activity on the myometrium, and the response is a slight decrease in amplitude (Table 4.I) (Sandberg et al., 1965).

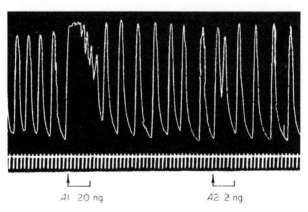

FIG. 4.4. Effects of component A1 (= $PGF_{2\alpha}$) and component A2 (= PGE_2) from human menstrual fluid on the contractions of a human myometrial preparation in vitro. The quantities quoted are only approximate, but they represent roughly the ratio of A1 to A2 in menstrual fluid. Time-marker, minutes; bath volume, 4 ml (after Pickles and Hall, 1963).

The effect of a total prostaglandin extract (HSF-PG) as well as of some crystalline prostaglandins on longitudinal muscle strips from various portions of the human fallopian tube has been studied by Sandberg et al. (1963a,b, 1964, 1965). The most

TABLE 4.I

SUMMARY OF THE EFFECTS EXERTED BY PROSTAGLANDINS ON THE
FALLOPIAN TUBE AND THE HUMAN UTERUS[a,b]

Prostaglandin	Fallopian tube segment				Uterus	
	1	2	3	4	Corpus	Isthmus
PGE_1	++	−−	−−	−−	−	−−
PGE_2	+	−−	−−	−−	−	−−
PGE_3	−	−−	−−	−−	−	−−
$PGF_{1\alpha}$	++	++	++	++	+	0
$PGF_{1\beta}$	+	+	+	+	−	(−)
$PGF_{2\alpha}$	+++	+++	+++	+++	++	+
$PGF_{2\beta}$	−	−	−	−	(−)	−

[a] A stimulatory effect is graded +++, ++, + and an inhibitory effect is graded
−−, −, (−).
[b] After Sandberg *et al.* (1965).

proximal part (segment No. 1) often reacts with increased tonus
and/or amplitude to HSF-PG, PGE_1, and PGE_2, although the
more distal segments (toward the ovary) respond with decreased
tonus and/or amplitude (Fig. 4.5, Table 4.1). $PGF_{1\alpha}$, $PGF_{1\beta}$, and
$PGF_{2\alpha}$ caused increased muscular activity in all segments, but

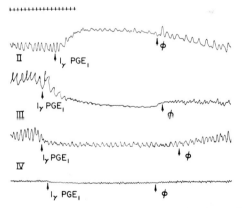

FIG. 4.5. The effect of PGE_1 (1 μg) on the longitudinal muscles of four segments of equal length from the human fallopian tube. Bath volume 20 ml. Top
curve from segment No. 1. Wash indicated by ϕ (after Sandberg *et al.*, 1963b).

$PGF_{1\beta}$ had a weak inhibitory effect when tested in the same dose range (0.006–0.20 μg/ml). The biological activities of the various compounds are summarized in Table 4.I.

The action of the prostaglandins on the isolated human myometrium is not affected by agents blocking the adrenergic α- or β-receptors (Eliasson, 1966a,b; Pickles *et al.*, 1966).

b. Pregnant Myometrium

The normal effect of HSF-PG on myometrium from the twelfth to the twentieth week of gestation is one of stimulation, although inhibition can sometimes be observed (von Euler, 1936; Bygdeman, 1964). Bygdeman (1964) found PGE_1 to cause stimulation of the motility with increased tonus in about half of the experiments with myometrium from early pregnancy (weeks 12–20), although further addition of E_1 could evoke a decrement in the spontaneous motility (Fig. 4.6).

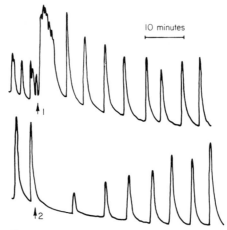

FIG. 4.6. The effect of PGE_1 on a strip from human myometrium during the fourth month of pregnancy: 1 = 0.01 μg/ml; 2 = 0.03 μg/ml (after Bygdeman, 1964).

$PGF_{1\alpha}$ stimulates the motility, and the sensitivity of the pregnant myometrium is markedly elevated in comparison with that of the nonpregnant uterus (Fig. 4.7) (Bygdeman, 1964). So far, there are no data available for the other prostaglandins.

The reactivity of the myometrium from full-term pregnancy to prostaglandins has apparently only been studied in a few instances. Bygdeman (1964) reports that 0.3 µg of PGE_1/ml of bath fluid produced no effect, although $PGF_{1\alpha}$ in doses of 0.01–0.5 µg/ml enhanced the motility.

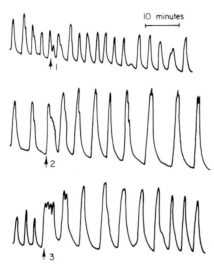

FIG. 4.7. The effect of $PGF_{1\alpha}$ on human isolated myometrium from a uterus in the fourth month of pregnancy: 1 = 0.01 µg/ml; 2 = 0.03 µg/ml; 3 = 0.3 µg/ml (after Bygdeman, 1964).

c. Influence of Posterior Pituitary Hormones

According to Csapo (1954), oxytocin exerts its stimulatory effect by sensitizing the myometrium to various intrinsic and extrinsic stimuli. It was also observed by Eliasson and Posse (1960) that the reactivity pattern of the intact, nonpregnant human uterus seemed to be different when the combined use of an intravenous infusion of a posterior pituitary hormone preparation and intravaginal application of prostaglandin (HSF-PG) was compared with that of prostaglandin alone (see Section A,2).

Addition of vasopressin and oxytocin alone or in combination, however, did not change the sensitivity or reaction pattern of the isolated nonpregnant human myometrium to prostaglandin E_1 (Eliasson, 1966c).

d. Influence of Ovarian Steroids

Quantitative assay of the effect of the total prostaglandin extract from human semen or the prostaglandin E on the motility of the human isolated myometrium has been based on the inhibitory action and expressed as "inhibitory dose 50" (ID_{50}), i.e., the smallest dose tested that for 10 minutes or more caused a decrease of the amplitude of the contractions of at least 50% (Bygdeman and Eliasson, 1963a).

The change in reactivity and sensitivity of the myometrium during the menstrual cycle and pregnancy, as briefly described above, indicates that the response to the prostaglandins is dependent on the endocrine status. Such a dependence has also been experimentally verified. Myometrial strips taken from patients in late proliferatory or early secretory phase are significantly more sensitive to the prostaglandins E—and consequently also to HSF-PG—than strips taken early or late in the menstrual cycle (Tables 4.II and 4.III). Moreover, the effect of prostaglandins seems to decrease with time after the onset of the menopause (Bygdeman and Eliasson, 1963a; Pickles and Hall, 1963; Bygdeman, 1964).

TABLE 4.II

VARIATIONS IN SENSITIVITY OF NONPREGNANT HUMAN
MYOMETRIUM TO HUMAN SEMINAL FLUID PROSTAGLANDIN EXTRACT
(HSF-PG) IN VITRO[a]

Hormonal status	HSF-PG ID_{50} (units/ml)	
	Median values	Range
Early-middle proliferative phase	0.015	0.0025–0.05
Late proliferative phase	0.0045	0.001–0.01
Early secretory phase	0.007	0.0025–0.03
Middle-late secretory phase	0.022	0.01–0.15

[a] After Bygdeman and Eliasson (1963a).

The myometrium seems, on the other hand, to be more sensitive to $PGF_{2\alpha}$ near the end of a menstrual cycle than at other times (Pickles and Hall, 1963).

Addition of progesterone to the bath fluid (10 μg/ml) causes a slight decrement of the sensitivity of the midcycle myometrium to PGE_1, though no effect was observed with progesterone added to myometrial strips taken during other periods of the menstrual cycle. No change in sensitivity or reactivity was noted after the addition of estradiol to the bath fluid (Bygdeman, 1964).

TABLE 4.III

VARIATIONS IN SENSITIVITY OF PREGNANT AND NONPREGNANT HUMAN MYOMETRIUM TO PGE_1 *in Vitro*[a]

Hormonal status	PGE_1 ID_{50} (μg/ml)	
	Median values	Range
Early-middle proliferative phase	0.05	0.03–0.1
Late proliferative phase	0.025	0.01–0.1
Early secretory phase	0.025	0.01–0.05
Middle-late secretory phase	0.05	0.02–0.5
Pregnancy	0.05	0.03–0.3

[a] After Bygdeman (1964).

e. Influence of Potassium and Calcium

The potassium concentration in the bath fluid, $[K_e]$, has a marked effect on the reactivity pattern of the isolated myometrium. A lowering of $[K_e]$ from 5.6 to 3.8 or 2.1 mEq/liter potentiated the inhibitory action of HSF-PG, although an increase in extracellular potassium concentration had the opposite effect. At $[K_e]$ above 12 mEq/liter, the response could even be reversed, i.e., HSF-PG enhanced the motility and tonus (Bygdeman and Eliasson, 1963c).

Bygdeman (1964) made a similar study using crystalline PGE_1 and $PGF_{1\alpha}$. An elevation of the potassium concentration resulted in a potentiation of the response to $PGF_{1\alpha}$ and a reduction to that of PGE_1 (Fig. 4.8). Consequently, a diminution of $[K_e]$ had the opposite effect. This difference in reactivity to the two prostaglandins seems to explain the reversed response to HSF-PG at high potassium concentrations described above.

These results would indicate that the membrane potential is of importance to the effect of the various prostaglandins. It is, however, of interest that similar changes in the potassium concentration do not affect the sensitivity or reactivity pattern to the adrenergic β-receptor-stimulating compound isoxsuprine that also causes inhibition of the spontaneous motility of the myometrium (Bygdeman and Eliasson, 1963d).

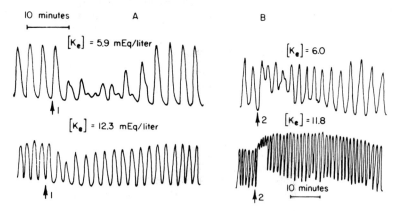

FIG. 4.8. Various effects of an increase in potassium concentration, $[K_e]$, on the reactivity pattern of isolated strips from human nonpregnant myometrium to prostaglandins. The response to PGE_1 (A: $1 = 0.01$ μg/ml) is diminished, but that to $PGF_{1\alpha}$ (B: $2 = 0.5$ μg/ml) is enhanced (after Bygdeman, 1964).

The calcium concentration in the bath fluid has been reported of importance to several prostaglandin actions. The influence on the myometrial response is, on the other hand, not marked. It appears that a decrease in calcium concentration to 1 mEq/liter would enhance the inhibitory effect of HSF-PG and PGE_1 on myometrial strips taken at midcycle (Bygdeman, 1964).

2. In Vivo

a. Intrauterine Pressure Recordings

The first study of the effect of human semen on the motility of the intact human uterus was performed by Karlson (1949, 1959). The intrauterine pressure was registered with small pressure-sensitive receptors on a probe locating the receptors in the fundus, isthmus, and cervix of uteri (Karlson, 1944). The investigation was carried out on seven infertile women and one patient admitted to the hospital with abdominal pain. Instillation of 0.25–1 ml of semen in the vagina or uterine cavity usually caused an increased motility of the corpus and a concomitant decrease in that of the cervix. In one patient, the motility of the corpus was markedly diminished, a reactivity pattern thought to be a possible explanation of her infertility. In this study, no determinations were made of the prostaglandin activity in the semen specimens used.

Eliasson and Posse (1960) carried out a similar study using the same registration technique, but their investigation was made on eight volunteers — fertile, healthy women between 23 and 35 years old. On each individual, four to five experiments were performed during various times in the menstrual cycles. Intravaginal instillation of partially purified prostaglandin (HSF-PG) in amounts corresponding to that usually found in ejaculates from healthy men (i.e., 150–200 units) had little or no effect on the uterine motility during menstruation, early in the proliferatory phase, or late in the secretory phase. On the other hand, prostaglandin caused an increase in the motility of the corpus in five of seven subjects at the estimated time of ovulation. In three cases, the increased activity was succeeded by a marked inhibition. In two women with this reactivity pattern, a similar experiment was carried out at the estimated time of ovulation in the following period, but on this occasion, an intravenous infusion of oxytocin and vasopressin (100–300 mU of each/minute) was started a few minutes before the intravaginal instillation of HSF-PG. Prostaglandin under these circumstances only caused a marked decrease in the motility (Figs. 4.9 and 4.10).

A similar experiment was carried out on the third woman, but in the proliferative phase. This was the only case in which prostaglandin had a stimulatory effect during this part of the menstrual cycle.

The reason for studying the combined effect of prostaglandin and the posterior pituitary hormones was 2-fold. First, there is evidence that a release of posterior pituitary hormones occurs during coitus (Pickles, 1953; Harris and Pickles, 1953; Campbell and Petersen, 1953; Friberg, 1953), and several authors (see Pickford, 1960) have suggested that oxytocin and vasopressin are liberated together following stimulation of the posterior pituitary gland. Second, Csapo (1954) has suggested that oxytocin increases the sensitivity of the myometrium to various intrinsic and extrinsic stimuli. In this connection it should be recalled that the nonpregnant human myometrium during the latter half of the menstrual cycle, in contrast to myometrium from our common laboratory animals, is most insensitive to oxytocin, but very sensitive to vasopressin (see Bygdeman and Eliasson, 1963e; Csapo and Pinto-Dantas, 1966; Joelsson *et al.*, 1966).

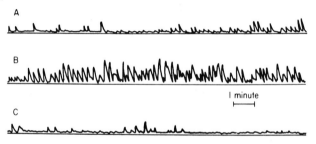

FIG. 4.9. Effect of prostaglandin on the motility of the human uterus *in vivo*. Registration from corpus at the time of ovulation: A, control period; B, 5–20 minutes after intravaginal application of 150 units of prostaglandin (HSF-PG); C, 25–40 minutes after the application of prostaglandin (after Eliasson and Posse, 1960).

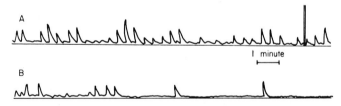

FIG. 4.10. Effect of prostaglandin on the motility of the human uterus *in vivo*, registration from the corpus at the time of ovulation. During the experiment an iv infusion of 0.1 IU of oxytocin + 0.1 IU of vasopressin per minute is given: A, control period; at signal, intravaginal application of 150 units of prostaglandin (HSF-PG); B, record from 6 to 21 minutes after the application of prostaglandin (after Eliasson and Posse, 1960).

The change in reactivity pattern observed in the experiments described above with the combined use of posterior pituitary hormones and prostaglandins seemed to support the Csapo hypothesis, i.e., that an increased sensitivity of the myometrium should result in an inhibition of the motility at lower prostaglandin concentration. One would thus compare this reactivity pattern with that *in vitro*, where a small amount of prostaglandin could have a stimulatory effect and a slightly larger amount an inhibitory action, as discussed in Section A,1.)

However, as already mentioned, addition of oxytocin and/or vasopressin to the bath fluid did not change the sensitivity or reactivity of isolated strips from human myometrium to prostaglandin. Therefore, we must ponder other modes of action. One possibility seems to be an enhanced absorption of prostaglandins from the vagina, since it is well known that vasopressin can increase the permeability of some mucous membranes (cf. Leaf and Hayes, 1961; Sawyer, 1961).

The effect of the various pure prostaglandin compounds on the intact human uterus is almost unexplored. Intrauterine application of $PGF_{2\alpha}$ causes a marked increase in the motility — a finding of interest with regard to the possible relation with the endometrial prostaglandins and dysmenorrhea (see Pickles *et al.*, 1966). Intravaginal applications of the PGE's (100–150 μg) have been recorded to cause decreased uterine motility in some women (Ingelman-Sundberg, personal communication). Intravenous infusion of PGE_1 (0.01–0.04 μg/kg/minute), to women in early pregnancy caused an increased motility of the uterus and an elevation of the intraamniotic pressure, recorded according to Caldeyro-Barcia (1958). There was a delayed onset and a slow disappearance of the effect. Pulse rate increased slightly, but blood pressure remained unchanged. Similar findings were noted on one patient at term pregnancy (Bygdeman *et al.*, 1967).

b. The Rubin Test

Insufflation of carbon dioxide into the uterine cavity is often used for studies of the functional patency of the oviducts (the Rubin test). At a constant flow rate, the pressure in the recording system is almost proportional to the resistance to the gas (Rubin, 1947). If the gas is introduced into the uterine cavity above the isthmus sphincter, the main resistance is present at the functional sphincters at the uterotubal junctions. This method was used by Eliasson and Posse (1965) in a study of the effect of seminal prostaglandins on the resistance to gas flow through the uterotubal junction and the fallopian tubes.

In four out of seven patients—all with unexplained infertility— intravaginal application of 150–200 units HSF-PG did not change the resistance to gas flow. In three other patients, there was a marked increase in the recorded pressure, i.e., in the resistance (Figs. 4.11 and 4.12). In one of the patients, after 25 minutes there was apparently a complete occlusion and the pressure rose to above 200 mm Hg at which point the valve had to be opened and the pressure released, since the patient complained

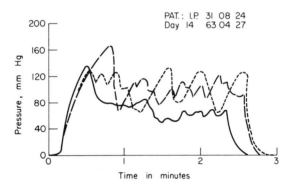

FIG. 4.11. Effect of prostaglandin on the Rubin test: —, control; . . ., and – –, 7 and 24 minutes, respectively, after intravaginal application of 150 units of prostaglandin (HSF-PG) (after Eliasson and Posse, 1965).

of severe pain. In another patient (Fig. 4.12), the pressure was raised stepwise until gas passed. In this experiment HSF-PG caused such an increase in the resistance that the pressure rose from 150 to 320 mm Hg. At this time, the valve was opened and the pressure released. The enhanced resistance to flow in these patients most likely owes to an increase in the tonus at the uterotubal junction.

It is, of course, not possible to decide which of the two response patterns observed should be regarded as "normal."
Further studies on fertile women are needed. In this connection,
it is of interest that Sandberg *et al.* (1963a,b,) reported that
HSF-PG and PGE$_1$ sometimes caused an increased motility of
the proximal end of the isolated fallopian tube, but a relaxation
of the more distal parts.

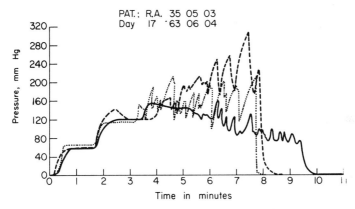

FIG. 4.12. Effect of prostaglandin on the Rubin test. —, control; . . ., and – –,
8 and 28 minutes, respectively, after intravaginal application of 200 units of
prostaglandin (HSF-PG) (after Eliasson and Posse, 1965).

3. PHYSIOLOGICAL CONSIDERATIONS

a. Seminal Prostaglandins

The anatomy, biochemistry, and physiology of mammalian reproduction reveal marked differences. With respect to the sperm
transport into the fallopian tubes, we can, however, distinguish
between two main groups of animals, one in which the spermatozoa are deposited at the ejaculation directly into the uterine
cavity or the cervical canal, and one in which the spermatozoa
are placed in the posterior portion of the vagina. In the second
group, we find, among others, cattle, sheep, rabbit, and man.

The vagina usually provides a hostile environment for the
sperm cells, and a rapid transport of the cells into the cervical
mucus and uterine cavity is therefore necessary. The ascent of

the spermatozoa can be a result of their own motility (active transport), the muscular activity in the vagina and uterus (passive transport), or a combination of both. There is ample evidence for a fast and passive migration of sperm cells as well as inert particles in cattle and rabbit.

In these species, the ascent of inert material can be evoked by a variety of factors such as mating, artificial stimulation of the genital organs, and infusion of oxytocin (Van Demark and Moeller, 1951; Van Demark and Hays, 1954; Rowson, 1955; Parkes, 1931; Krehbiel and Carstens, 1938). The time interval necessary for the spermatozoa to migrate from the vagina into the oviducts in the cow was estimated to be about 5 minutes by Van Demark and Moeller (1951).

The rapid sperm transport in the genital tract of the ewe following normal service of the ram strongly supports the opinion that a passive migration also occurs in this species (Schott and Phillips, 1941; Starke, 1949; Mattner, 1963a,b; Mattner and Braden, 1963).

There are divergent opinions with respect to the possible occurrence of a passive sperm migration in man (cf. Hartman, 1957; Sobrero and MacLeod, 1962). Arguments in favor of such a mechanism have, however, been forwarded by several authors. Belonoschkin (1949) claims that spermatozoa can be found in the uterine cavity within a few minutes after ejaculation if the woman has experienced orgasm. Transport of inert particles from the vagina into the uterine cavity in connection with coitus has been reported by Amersbach (1930), Trapl (1943), and Egli and Newton (1961). Asplund (1952) observed that during hysterograms made in the middle of the menstrual cycle, the radioopaque medium quickly passed from the uterus into the abdominal cavity in a remarkably large number of cases. This observation suggests the occurrence of an antiperistaltic movement in the uterus and oviducts. A correlation between sperm migration and the uterine motility pattern was further reported by Bickers (1951).

During sexual stimulation and orgasm, there is a marked increase in the recorded uterine activity and in the intrauterine pressure (Masters and Johnson, 1966, p. 116). This reactivity pattern, the large amount of prostaglandins normally present in human semen, the high sensitivity of the myometrium to the prostaglandins at the time of ovulation, and the effects of prostaglandins on uterine motility strongly suggest that these factors play an important role in human reproduction.

One possibility could be that the uterine activity during coitus causes a movement of the cervical mucus that brings attached spermatozoa into the cervical canal. The action of prostaglandins might facilitate this as well as the intrauterine migration (Eliasson, 1959).

The proper study of these problems is, however, hampered by insufficiency in the present recording devices as well as the fact that psychological factors markedly influence the motility and reactivity patterns of the human uterus.

b. Endometrial Prostaglandins

The human endometrium and menstrual fluid contain the so-called menstrual stimulant factor, the main principle of which is prostaglandin $F_{2\alpha}$. The menstrual stimulant increases the uterine motility and tonus of the human uterus *in vivo* and *in vitro*, and the myometrium is most sensitive at the end of the menstrual cycle. It was therefore pertinent to look at the relation between this factor and dysmenorrhea. Pickles *et al.* (1965) compared the prostaglandin content in menstrual fluid from seven patients with primary dysmenorrheas with that from normal women. The total activity in the material obtained from the dysmenorrheic patients was, however, on the average not significantly different from that obtained by extraction from a large number of pooled specimens. The individual values from the dysmenorrheic patients showed, on the other hand, a wide variability.

Progesterone seems to increase the prostaglandin production by the endometrium. It may also enhance dysmenorrheas. Anovulatory cycles are generally without pain. These observations are in consonance with the hypothesis that the sensitivity of the myometrium to prostaglandins F or the amount of prostaglandins F produced by the endometrium may play a role in dysmenorrheas (Pickles *et al.*, 1965; Hall, 1966).

It has also been propounded that the endometrial prostaglandins could be of importance to implantation of the fertilized ovum (Pickles and Hall, 1963).

B. Other Smooth-Muscle Organs

1. GASTROINTESTINAL TRACT

The smooth muscles of the gastrointestinal tract are stimulated by the various prostaglandins. In contrast to the prompt response following treatment with acetylcholine or histamine, there is usually a delayed onset following the administration of the prostaglandins. In general, the sensitivity of the muscles is high and the threshold doses for PGE_1 are often in the order of 5–50 ng/ml of bath fluid. There are, however, marked species variations, as illustrated in Table 4.IV. Relative activities between various prostaglandins are also given in the text.

The biological effects on isolated rabbit jejunum and guinea pig ileum of dehydro-PGE_1, 15-keto-PGE_1, and 15-ketodehydro-PGE_1 are qualitatively the same as those of PGE_1, but the metabolites are only 1–30% as active (Änggård, 1966b).

The biological properties of nor-PGE_1 are qualitatively similar to those of PGE_1. In comparison with PGE_1 (=1), the activity ratio on isolated rabbit jejunum, guinea pig ileum, and rat fundus is 0.1–0.3 : 1 (Horton and Main, 1966a).

The qualitative response to $PGF_{1\beta}$ is the same as that for $PGF_{1\alpha}$. The activity ratio on the isolated smooth muscles of the gastrointestinal tract is, in relation to $PGF_{1\alpha}$, between 0.05 and 0.1 (Horton and Main, 1966b). A number of prostaglandin analogs have been tested for their biological activity on rabbit and guinea pig intestinal smooth muscles, rat blood pressure, and antilipolytic effect on rat fat pad (Pike et al., 1967).

Rabbit duodenum and jejunum as well as hamster colon respond in a specific manner to the various prostaglandins and have often been used for bioassay of prostaglandin activity in partially purified extracts (Fig. 4.13). The isolated ascending colon from the jird (Meriones tristrami and M. shawi) has also been found suitable for bioassay of prostaglandins and related compounds (Ambache, 1966). The sensitivity of the preparations from the small desert rodents to PGE_2 is of the order of 0.1–1

TABLE 4.IV

BIOLOGICAL ACTIVITY OF VARIOUS PROSTAGLANDINS ON SOME ISOLATED SMOOTH-MUSCLE ORGANS

Test organ	Threshold dose of PGE_1 (ng/ml)	Activity in relation to $PGE_1 = 1$				Threshold dose $PGF_{2\alpha}$ (ng/ml)	References
		PGE_2	PGE_3	$PGF_{1\alpha}$	$PGF_{2\alpha}$		
Rabbit jejunum	3–10			1–3			Bergström et al., 1959b
	–	3.5	0.4				Bergström and von Euler, 1963
							Horton and Main, 1963, 1965b
	12	1.5	0.99	2.2	26	0.5–1	Änggård and Bergström, 1963
Guinea pig ileum	10–20						Bergström et al., 1959b
	–	0.4–1.3	0.15	0.03			Bergström and von Euler, 1963
							Horton and Main, 1963, 1965b
	8	1.6	0.20	0.02	0.55	25	Änggård and Bergström, 1963
Rat jejunum	10–30			0.1			Bergström et al., 1959b
							Horton, 1963
Rat duodenum	250					125	Änggård and Bergström, 1963
Rat colon						125	Änggård and Bergström, 1963
							Coceani and Wolfe, 1965
Rat stomach fundus	0.1–0.5						Horton and Main, 1963; 1965b
Hamster colon	12	2.8	0.2	0.3	3.5	1–5	Bergström et al., 1959b
Chick jejunum	8			0.025			Bergström et al., 1959b
Chick rectal caecum	7			0.3–2		5	Änggård and Bergström, 1963

ng/ml. One of them is even sensitive to 14–56 ng of the C_{16} nor-PGE$_1$ (Ambache *et al.*, 1966b).

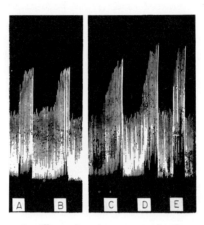

FIG. 4.13. Spasmogenic effect of various prostaglandin preparations on the isolated rabbit jejunum. Bath volume, 15 ml. A, 0.3 µg of PGE$_1$; B, 0.1 µg of PGF$_{1\alpha}$; C, 2 µg of the barium salt of prostaglandin, according to von Euler, (1939); D, 0.02 "units" of a total prostaglandin extract from sheep vesicular gland, according to Eliasson (1959); E, 0.5 µg of PGE$_1$ (after Bergström *et al.*, 1959b).

Superfused rat stomach fundus is also a useful test preparation, although sometimes a slight tachyphylaxis is noted (Coceani and Wolfe, 1966). The sensitivity to PGE$_1$ is of the order of 0.1–0.5 ng/ml. In their study of the mode of action, Wolfe and co-workers found atropine, hyoscine, 5-hydroxytryptamine to be antagonists, and papaverine (3×10^{-7} gm/ml) without specific effect on the prostaglandin response. Pretreatment with procaine (10^{-5} gm/ml) (Fig. 4.14), xylocaine, and bretylium tosylate, as well as increase in the calcium and/or potassium concentrations in the bath fluid, potentiated the response. A number of other conditions were also found to potentiate the prostaglandin action, for example, the addition to the superfusion fluid of reduced glutathione (10^{-4} gm/ml), ascorbic acid (10^{-4} gm/ml), and sodium fluoride (10^{-5} gm/ml). Among the conditions that decreased the response to PGE$_1$ were addition of adrenaline, noradrenaline, sodium cyanide (8×10^{-6} gm/ml), α-adrenergic receptor blocking agents, reserpine treatment, carbon monoxide, and hypoxia. The authors suggested that the prostaglandins were taken up by the tissue during the anoxic period, but could not induce any contraction without the presence of oxygen. The hypothesis that prostaglandins in association with an oxygen-requiring metabolic reaction initiate contractions by the release of bound calcium or by the facilitation of calcium influx was proposed by Coceani and Wolfe (1966) and Wolfe *et al.* (1967).

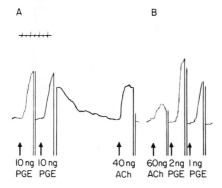

A   B

10 ng 10 ng   40 ng   60ng 2ng 1ng
PGE PGE   ACh   ACh PGE PGE

FIG. 4.14. The effect of procaine·HCl on the action of prostaglandin E_1 and acetylcholine on the isolated rat-stomach fundus strip. Perfusion with Tyrode solution. Bath volume, 9 ml. Temperature, 37°C. Time scale, 30 seconds. A, 10 ng of prostaglandin E_1 (the second record illustrates the prolonged period of increased muscle tone) and 40 ng of acetylcholine added before procaine; B, procaine hydrochloride, 1×10^{-5} gm/ml added to the Tyrode solution and the muscle superfused 2 hours; 60 ng of acetylcholine and then 2 ng and 1 ng of prostaglandin E_1 added. The preparation is less sensitive to acetylcholine, but almost ten times more sensitive to prostaglandin E_1 (after Coceani and Wolfe, 1966).

Guinea pig ileum is less suitable for bioassay since it often shows tachyphylaxis with prostaglandin extracts (Eliasson, unpublished observation) and with $PGF_{2\alpha}$ (Fig. 4.15) (Änggård and Bergström, 1963). The spasmogenic effect of the partially purified extracts on the guinea pig ileum was not affected by specific doses of atropine, antihistaminics, hexamethonium, *d*-tubocurarine, nicotine, cocaine, tryptamine, lysergic acid diethylamide (LSD-25), or dihydroergotamine. In some experiments, hexamethonium and cocaine potentiated the response to the prostaglandin extracts. The only substance found that inhibited the spasmogenic effect of the prostaglandin extract was patulin. The effects of acetylcholine, histamine, 5-hydroxytryptamine, and nicotine were likewise suppressed, but that of barium chloride was unchanged. The stimulatory effect of substance P was usually potentiated (Eliasson, 1958b, 1959, unpublished observation) (cf. Section 4,F).

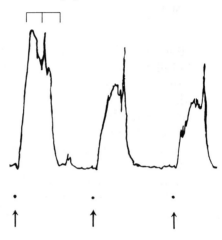

FIG. 4.15. Spasmogenic effect of $PGF_{2\alpha}$ (1 μg at arrow) on isolated guinea pig ileum. Note the tendency to tachyphylaxis. Bath volume, 15 ml Tyrode solution with 1.5×10^{-6} M atropine. Time in minutes (after Änggård and Bergström, 1963).

The mode of action of the crystalline prostaglandins on the guinea pig ileum does not seem to have been looked into closely, but Horton (1965) suggested that part of the activity of PGE_1 was mediated by a nervous pathway since the effect was partially antagonized by atropine (10^{-8} gm/ml).

Prostaglandin E_1 causes a contraction of the isolated guinea pig taenia coli and at the same time markedly increases the spike potentials (Miyazaki et al., 1967). The same author also reported that botulinus toxin (type C) in doses inhibiting the stimulatory effect of nicotine on isolated rabbit jejunum did not affect the response to PGE_1 or acetylcholine. PGE_1 had no effect on the potassium depolarized rabbit duodenum; this suggests that the electrical activity of the muscle membrane is of importance for the action (Sasamori, 1965; Miyazaki *et al.*, 1967). PGE_1 was also ineffective when the rabbit duodenum was placed in calcium-free solution (Sasamori, 1965).

So far, no evidence for a physiological role for prostaglandins in the gastrointestinal tract has been forwarded.

2. RESPIRATORY TRACT

a. In Vivo

Intravenous injection of 15–50 μg of $PGF_{2\alpha}$ increases the pulmonary resistance to inflation (compliance) in cats (see Fig. 4.33) (Änggård and Bergström, 1963) and guinea pig (Berry and Collier, 1964). It is likely that this owes to vascular congestion rather than to a direct effect on the bronchial musculature, since the isolated tracheal and bronchial muscles of the cat and guinea pig seem to be rather insensitive to $PGF_{2\alpha}$ (Änggård and Bergström, 1963; Änggård, 1966a; Horton and Main, 1965b). The "resistance to inflation" or "compliance" was studied by measuring the volume of air that, during artificial respiration and constant pressure did not enter the lung ("tidal overflow volume"). PGE_1 increased the compliance in cat when injected in doses as low as 0.3 μg/kg, but lowered (1.6 μg of PGE_1/kg) the resistance to inflation in rabbits. In the rabbit it also decreased the pulmonary response to electrical stimulation of the vagal nerves (Fig. 4.16) (Main, 1964). In guinea pig, PGE_1 (0.1–0.25 μg/kg) antagonized the response to vagal stimulation and histamine (Fig. 4.17) (Main, 1964), but had no effect by itself (Horton, 1963).

Although PGE_1 caused a transient slowing of the respiratory rate in the chick, $PGF_{2\alpha}$ had no such effect (Horton and Main, 1965c).

b. Isolated Preparations

The action of PGE_1 on isolated tracheal muscle preparations from monkey, sheep, pig, ferret, cat, rabbit, and guinea pig has been investigated by Main (1964). An inhibitory effect on the spontaneous tone was found in organs from guinea pig and ferret (threshold dose 0.005–0.1 μg/ml), although no effect was seen on preparations from the pig and sheep. The tracheal muscles from monkey, cat, and rabbit did not show any inherent tone *in vitro.*

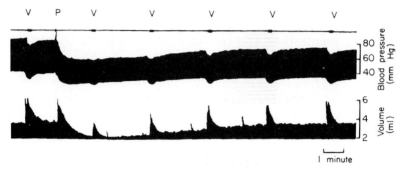

FIG. 4.16. Inhibitory effect of PGE₁ (P = 4 μg iv) on the "resistance to pulmonary inflation" following electrical stimulation of the vagal nerve (V = stimulation for 10 seconds) in a urethan-anesthetized rabbit. From above: events marker; arterial blood pressure; tidal overflow volume (after Main, 1964).

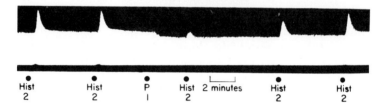

FIG. 4.17. Inhibitory effect of PGE₁ (P) on the histamine-induced (Hist) bronchoconstriction in a urethan-anesthetized guinea pig. The curve shows the tidal overflow volume. All doses are given in micrograms, and the compounds were injected intravenously (after Main, 1964).

An elevation of the muscle tone in the various tracheal preparations could be induced by adding acetycholine (all species), histamine (guinea pig), dihydroergotamine (cat), or barium chloride (cat, monkey, guinea pig, ferret, and sheep). This elevation of the tone could usually be counteracted by PGE₁, as illustrated in Figs. 4.18 and 4.19. Nor-PGE₁ had the same action as PGE₁. The activity ratio nor-PGE₁/PGE₁ was 0.1. The various results are summarized in Table 4.V (Main, 1964).

Prostaglandins E₂, E₃, and F₁ₐ antagonized the acetylcholine-induced contraction on cat isolated tracheal preparations. Their activities were, in relation to E_1 (=1), 1.0, 0.2, and 0.002 (Main, 1964).

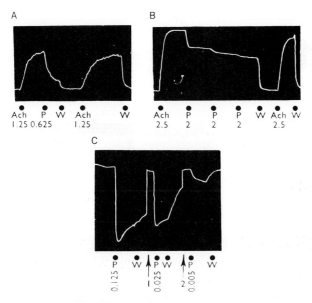

FIG. 4.18. Responses of isolated trachea preparations suspended in 4-ml organ baths containing Krebs-Henseleit solution: A, monkey; B, rabbit; C, ferret. Ach = acetylcholine; P = prostaglandin E_1; W = wash. All drug concentrations are in micrograms per milliliter. At arrows 1 and 2, the drum was stopped for 20 and 10 minutes, respectively (after Main, 1964).

The predominant smooth muscle-stimulating prostaglandin in lung tissue is $PGF_{2\alpha}$, and the amount present is of the same order as that of noradrenaline. It is therefore understandable that much research is devoted to elucidation of the possible physiological function of this compound in lung tissue. It should, however, be recalled that at least sheep lungs also contain PGE_2—a compound that, in a concentration of 1 ng/ml, counteracts the acetylcholine-induced contraction in isolated tracheal preparations from cats. On the same test preparation, the activity of $PGF_{2\alpha}$ was only about a thirtieth of that of E_1 or E_2 (Horton and Main,

1965b). The possibility that the PGE's may play a role thus also deserves further consideration.

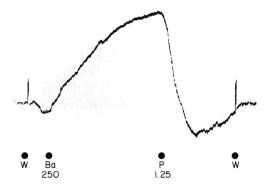

FIG. 4.19. Responses of an isolated guinea pig trachea preparation suspended in a 4-ml organ bath containing Krebs-Henseleit solution. Ba = barium chloride; P = prostaglandin E_1; W = wash. Drug concentrations in micrograms per milliliter (after Main, 1964).

TABLE 4.V

THRESHOLD CONCENTRATIONS OF PROSTAGLANDIN E_1 CAUSING INHIBITION
OF TONE IN ISOLATED TRACHEAL MUSCLE PREPARATIONS[a,b]

	Threshold concentration of prostaglandin acting (μg/ml)				
	Contraction owing to				
Species	Acetyl-choline	Dihydro-ergotamine	Barium chloride	Histamine	Inherent tone
Cat	0.001	0.001	0.25	✿	✿
Monkey	0.02	✿	2.5	✿	✿
Rabbit	0.05	✿	✿	✿	✿
Guinea pig	0.005	✿	0.25	0.005	0.005
Ferret	0.005	✿	0.25	✿	0.005
Sheep	3.0	✿	0.05	✿	1.0
Pig	0.25	✿	✿	✿	2.0

[a] Asterisks indicate that no inhibition could be demonstrated since the preparation had no initial tone even in the presence of the stimulant compound added. Values are μg/ml of prostaglandin E_1, which inhibited tone in the presence of the stimulants indicated.

[b] After Main (1964).

3. REPRODUCTIVE TRACT

a. Sheep

The influence of prostaglandins on the "intraluminal pressure" of the ewe oviduct—or maybe more correctly the intraluminal resistance to flow of Tyrode solution through the oviduct (infusion rate, 54 or 108 μl/minute)—has been studied by Horton *et al.* (1963, 1965). They found that both HSF-PG and PGE$_1$ produced changes in the pressure curves when injected intravenously or into the aorta. In three of the ewes there was an increase in the intraluminal resistance to flow, in two others a decrease (Figs. 4.20 and 4.21). There was no correlation between the reactivity pattern and the hormonal status or the time of the year. Intraaortic injection of 1 ml of ram semen (prostaglandin activity equivalent to 10 μg of PGE$_1$) was either without effect or caused only a slight transient increase in tubal tone (Fig. 4.21).

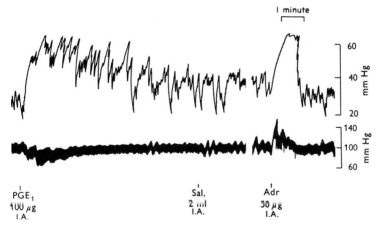

FIG. 4.20. Effect of prostaglandin E$_1$ injected into the aorta on the "intraluminal resistance to flow" through the oviduct of a pentobarbitone-anesthetized ewe (upper trace). Lower trace, arterial blood pressure. Sal = saline; Adr = adrenaline (after Horton *et al.*, 1965).

The isolated ewe oviduct responded to prostaglandins in the same way that it had *in situ*. The concentrations required to produce an effect ranged from 2.5 to 800 ng of PGE$_1$-equivalents/ml.

The oviducts that responded with relaxation seemed to be more sensitive. $PGF_{1\alpha}$ was tested on one preparation in a dose of 1000 ng/ml without any recorded effect. The various results are summarized in Table 4.VI (Horton *et al.*, 1963, 1965).

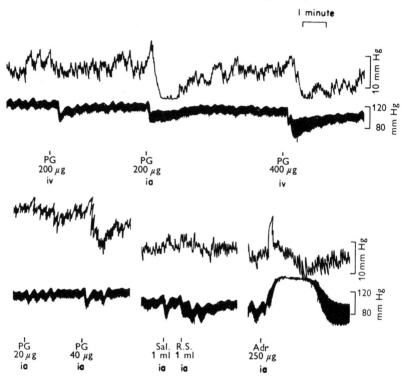

FIG. 4.21. Effect of prostaglandins on the "intraluminal resistance to flow" through the oviduct of a pentobarbital-anesthetized ewe (upper trace in each panel). Lower trace, arterial blood pressure. PG = crude prostaglandin mixture from human semen (activity expressed as PGE_1 equivalents) injected intravenously (iv) or intraaortically (ia). Sal = saline; Adr = adrenaline; R.S. = ram semen (after Horton *et al.*, 1965).

From the relative insensitivity of the oviducts of the anesthetized ewe to prostaglandins, Horton *et al.* (1965) concluded that the blood levels likely to be achieved at coitus would be far too small to affect the smooth muscle tone of the oviduct. The effect

TABLE 4.VI. EFFECTS AND EFFECTIVE DOSES OF PROSTAGLANDIN ON THE INTRALUMINAL RESISTANCE TO FLOW OF THE OVIDUCT in Situ AND in Vitro AND ON THE ARTERIAL BLOOD PRESSURE IN EWES[a]

Ewe No.	Wt (kg)	Hormonal pretreatment	Month of experiment	Oviduct in situ			Approximate threshold depressor doses (μg/kg) on intraaortic injection	Oviduct in vitro	
				Response	Effective intraaortic dose (μg/kg)[b]	Intraaortic infusion (μg/kg/min)		Response	Effective concentrations (ng/ml)[b]
1	55	None	March	—	—	—	—	Relaxation (sometimes preceded by contraction)	300–400
2	92	None	April	Contraction	0.4–1.7	—	0.2	Contraction	800
3	56	Stilbestrol	April	Relaxation	0.9–2.1	—	<0.9	Relaxation (after latent period)	100–200
4	76	Progesterone and PMS	May	Contraction	1.0–4.0	—	<0.7	No effect	>1000
5	40	Progesterone and PMS	November	Relaxation (preceded by transient contraction)	1.0–5.0	0.7, No effect 1.4, Relaxation 1.4, Relaxation	0.7 μg/kg/minute (intraaortic infusion)	Relaxation	2.5–40 (Prostaglandin E$_1$)
6	39	Progesterone and PMS	November	Contraction	2.5–5.0	2.2, No effect 4.3, Contraction 4.3, Contraction	2.2 μg/kg/minute (intraaortic infusion)	Relaxation (sometimes contraction)	100–4000
7	40	Progesterone and PMS	November	—	—	—	—	Relaxation	80

[a] After Horton et al. (1965).   [b] The lower figure in each range represents the approximate threshold dose or concentration.

of the ram seminal prostaglandins on the cervix and the uterine motility has, however, still to be determined.

In this connection it should be recalled that PGE_1 following intravenous infusion accumulates to an appreciable extent in the myometrium, oviducts, and ovaries of sheep (Samuelsson, 1965b). There is also a possibility that the sexual act in some way sensitizes the myometrium to prostaglandin (cf. Section 4,F).

b. Rabbit

The effect of HSF-PG on rabbit uterus *in vivo* was studied by Asplund (1947b) and Eliasson (1959). Intravenous infusion of prostaglandin usually changed the intrauterine pressure and the longitudinal contractions. The reactivity pattern was, however, qualitatively inconsistent. In some rabbits, prostaglandin increased the motility and the intrauterine pressure, in others a decrease was recorded. The response pattern was not correlated to the hormonal pretreatment and sometimes the effect was reversed during the experiment, as illustrated in Fig. 4.22.

Horton *et al.* (1963, 1965) studied the effect of prostaglandins on rabbit female reproductive tract with a method similar to that used in ewes. A polyethylene catheter was introduced into the uterus or oviduct. Tyrode solution was infused at a constant rate and could escape either through the infundibular end of the oviduct, through an incision in the uterine horn, or through the cervix, depending upon what part of the tract was studied. The pressure was recorded from a T-tube in the cannula.

In urethan-anesthetized animals, intravenous injections of PGE_1 (0.5–1.0 μg/kg) lowered the resistance to flow and reduced the amplitude and frequency of the contractions in the oviducts, uterine horns, and cervix (Fig. 4.23). The oviducts were most sensitive and the uterine horns least sensitive to prostaglandins. Pretreatment with estrogen could increase the sensitivity of the oviducts up to ten times. The same effect on the motility of the reproductive tract was observed even if the prostaglandin was injected intravaginally or intraperitoneally. The threshold dose of prostaglandin E_1 that produced an effect on intravaginal administration was 50–100 μg. Similar results were obtained by Asplund

(1947b) who used a continuous flow of carbon dioxide instead of Tyrode solution to study the resistance in the intact rabbit oviduct.

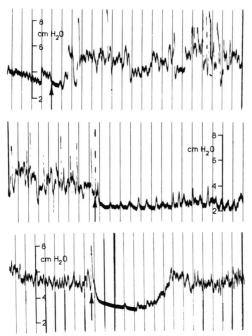

FIG. 4.22. Effect of seminal prostaglandins on the intraluminal pressure of an ovarectomized, stilbestrol- and progestrone-treated rabbit uterus *in vivo*. Time marking, 1 minute. Between records, 30 minutes. At arrows, iv injection of 2.5 "units" of a total prostaglandin extract from human seminal fluid (after Eliasson, 1959).

Intravenous injections of PGE_2 and PGE_3 had effects similar to those of PGE_1; PGE_2 was equiactive with PGE_1, and PGE_3 was half as active. Nor-PGE_1 had the same effect and was about one tenth as active. In contrast, injection of $PGF_{1\alpha}$ or $PGF_{2\alpha}$ in doses of 5 µg/kg usually increased the tone of the rabbit fallopian tubes (Horton and Main, 1963, 1965b).

Electrical stimulation *in vivo* of the efferent hypogastric nerve fibers to the isthmus of the rabbit oviduct causes occlusion of its lumen by constriction of the circular musculature in the isthmic wall (Brundin, 1965). It has recently been demonstrated that this effect is efficiently blocked by intravenous injection of 1 μg of PGE$_1$/kg (Brundin, personal communication).

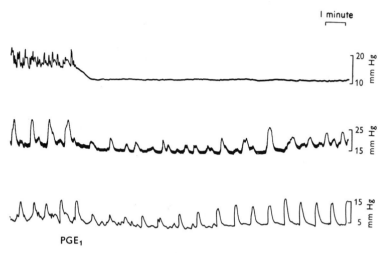

FIG. 4.23. Records of the "intraluminal resistance to flow" in the oviduct (upper trace), uterine horn (middle trace), and cervix (lower trace) of a urethan-anesthetized rabbit. PGE$_1$ = 6 μg of PGE$_1$ injected iv (after Horton *et al.*, 1965).

Isolated uteri from rabbits in normal or artificial estrus usually responded to HSF-PG with a decrease in spontaneous activity. On the other hand, increased activity can also be recorded. Similar results were obtained with uteri from animals that had been pretreated with both estrogen and progesterone. There seems to be no obvious correlation between the experimental conditions and the type of response, as is illustrated in Fig. 4.24. The two animals used for the experiments were of the same age and were treated in the same way—one still responded with a decrease, whereas the other one showed an increase in activity. The sensitivity of the rabbit myometrium to prostaglandins was about the same as that of the human. The isolated uterus from pseudopregnant rabbits responded with increased tone and amplitude of the contraction to partially purified prostaglandin. These uterine preparations were about ten times less sensitive to prostaglandins than those of estrogen-treated animals (Elias-son, 1959).

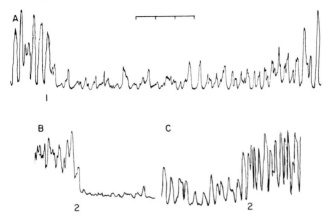

FIG. 4.24. Variation in effects of prostaglandin on isolated rabbit uterus. The two does were ovarectomized and pretreated with 30 μg of stilbestrol and 3 mg of progesterone for 3 days. Bath volume, 15 ml. Time marking, 2 minutes. A and B, records from the same uterus: 1 = 0.1 "unit"; 2 = 0.4 "unit" prostaglandin extract from sheep vesicular glands (after Eliasson, 1959).

The isolated rabbit oviduct possesses little inherent tone when perfused with a cannula placed in the lumen. Addition of adrenaline increases the tone, an action that can be counteracted by PGE_1 (see Fig. 4.51) (Horton *et al.*, 1965) (cf. Section 4,F).

The longitudinal muscle of the isolated rabbit oviduct is about as sensitive as the muscle of human corpus uteri to the inhibitory effect of PGE_1 (Pickles, personal communication).

The motility of the isolated rabbit uterus (normal estrus) was inhibited by both PGE_1 and $PGF_{1\alpha}$ and the organs sometimes showed marked tachyphylaxis against these two prostaglandins (Fig. 4.25). On the other hand, the total prostaglandin extract from sheep vesicular glands (containing PGE_1, PGE_2, PGE_3, as well as $PGF_{1\alpha}$ and $PGF_{2\alpha}$) stimulated the uterine motility, and the uterus did not show any tachyphylaxis (Eliasson, 1959).

The adrenaline-induced contractions of the vas deferens of rabbit and those evoked by electrical stimulations of the hypogastric nerves are inhibited both *in vivo* and *in vitro* by PGE_1 (Horton *et al.*, 1963; Mantegazza and Naimzada, 1965). No data seem to be available about the direct effect of the various prostaglandins on the male genital tract of rabbits.

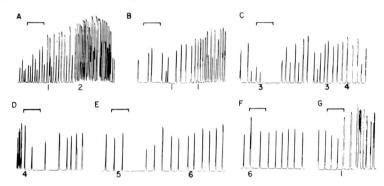

FIG. 4.25. Effect of a prostaglandin extract from sheep vesicular gland, prostaglandin E_1 and $F_{1\alpha}$, on the isolated uterus from a rabbit in normal estrus. Bath volume, 15 ml. Time marking, 5 minutes. The crude prostaglandin extract has a stimulating action (A, B, and G) and shows no tachyphylaxis: $1 = 0.1$ "unit"; $2 = 0.2$ "unit." PGE_1 has an inhibitory action (C and D), which, however, is lacking if the substance is again added without washing: $3 = 0.5$ μg; $4 = 1$ μg PGE_1. $PGF_{1\alpha}$, like PGE_1, shows an inhibitory action as well as tachyphylaxis (E and F): $5 = 0.5$ μg; $6 = 1$ μg $PGF_{1\alpha}$ (after Eliasson, 1959).

c. Guinea Pig

Isolated uteri from guinea pig respond with increase in tone and motility to both the PGE's and PGF's. The myometrium is more sensitive to the PGE's than to the PGF's. The threshold dose for E_1 is of the order of 0.2–0.5 ng/ml (Clegg *et al.*, 1966; Sullivan, 1966) and for $PGF_{2\alpha}$ about 5–10 ng/ml (Änggård and Bergström, 1963; Sullivan, 1966).

There is usually a latent period of 0.5–3 minutes after the addition of prostaglandin before the contractions begin; the period is shorter after addition of higher concentrations of the stimulant.

The mechanical activity following the addition of PGE_1 is accompanied by depolarization and spiking, as illustrated in Fig. 4.26 (Clegg *et al.*, 1966).

The guinea pig myometrium sometimes shows a decreased motility for up to 20 minutes after a given dose of PGE_1 or PGE_2 has been washed out of the organ bath. The uterus is, however, not inexcitable during this time; other stimulants give rise to an enhanced response, as will be described below (Section 4,F) (Clegg *et al.*, 1966).

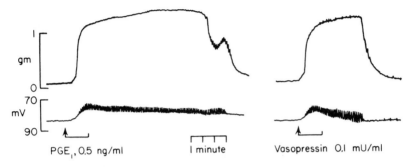

FIG. 4.26. Effect of prostaglandin E_1 and vasopressin on the tension (upper record) and membrane potential (lower record) of metestrous guinea pig myometrial preparation in sucrose-gap apparatus; ink tracing of ultraviolet record. The detail of the compound spikes was too fine for accurate reproduction. There was a gap of 17 minutes between the two sections (after Clegg *et al.*, 1966).

Estradiol alone or in combination with progesterone decreases the sensitivity of the castrate guinea pig uterus to the direct spasmogenic effect of both PGE_1 and $PGF_{2\alpha}$ (Pickles *et al.*, 1966), but has no effect on the action of prostaglandins on electrically stimulated preparations (Sullivan, 1966).

The sensitivity of the guinea pig myometrium to PGE_1 and PGE_2 is increased if the $[Ca^{2+}]$ in the suspending medium is elevated, but a decrease below the normal calcium concentration (1 mM) does not significantly alter the spontaneous response. $[Mg^{2+}]$ had the opposite effect; an elevation from 3 to 10 mEq/liter decreased the sensitivity to prostaglandins despite the fact that the response to vasopressin was potentiated (Pickles *et al.*, 1966). A lowering of the potassium concentration decreases the contraction following prostaglandin treatment, but an increase to 15 mM only seemed to enhance the prostaglandin effect (Pickles *et al.*, 1966).

The enhancement phenomenon described by Pickles *et al.* will be discussed in Section 4,F.

The isolated guinea pig seminal vesicles respond to PGE_1 in doses above 0.3 $\mu g/ml$ of bath fluid with contraction, but no response was found in a few experiments with $PGF_{1\alpha}$ in doses up to 1.2 $\mu g/ml$ (Eliasson and Risley, 1966, 1967). In doses 10–20 times smaller, PGE_1 potentiated the adrenaline-, noradrenaline-, and acetylcholine-induced contractions in the same preparation. A similar effect was noted on guinea pig vas deferens both *in situ* and *in vitro* by Mantegazza and Naimzada (1965) (see also Section 4,F).

Decreasing the calcium content in the bath fluid to half the normal concentration markedly reduces the mechanical response of the electrically stimulated, isolated guinea pig vas deferens. Addition of 0.5 μg of PGE_1/ml of bath fluid restores the reactivity to normal. This indicates that prostaglandin E_1 may affect the transport of calcium through the cell membranes (Mantegazza and Naimzada, 1965).

d. Rat

The isolated rat uterus responds with contraction to the various prostaglandins, but, in contrast to the guinea pig myometrium, the rat uterus seems to be more sensitive to $PGF_{2\alpha}$. The threshold dose for an increase in the spontaneous activity is about 60 ng of E_1/ml and 10–50 ng of $F_{2\alpha}/ml$ (Eliasson, 1959; Bergström *et al.*, 1959b; Änggård and Bergström, 1963; Horton, 1963; Horton and Main, 1963, 1965b, 1966a; Pickles *et al.*, 1966). The response of the uterus to electrical stimulation is increased in the presence of prostaglandins; the threshold dose for PGE_1 is 10 ng/ml and for $PGF_{2\alpha}$ is 0.5–1 ng/ml (Clegg, 1966a; Sullivan, 1966). The threshold doses and activity ratios for the different prostaglandins are summarized in Tables 4.VII and 4.VIII. It should be noted that nor-PGE_1 is equiactive with PGE_1 on the isolated rat uterus, although on other test organs it was only 0.1–0.33 as active.

Änggård and Bergström (1963) found the rat uterus more sensitive to $PGF_{2\alpha}$ than did Horton and Main (1963). It is pos-

TABLE 4.VII
THRESHOLD DOSES (MEAN VALUES) FOR SOME PROSTAGLANDINS WHEN
TESTED ON ISOLATED RAT UTERUS

Prosta-glandin	Hormonal status or treatment	Method	Threshold dose (ng/ml)	References
E_1	Stilbestrol	Spontaneous contraction	60	Horton, 1963; Horton and Main, 1963
	Estrus or estradiol	Electrical stimulation	10	Sullivan, 1966
$F_{1\alpha}$		Spontaneous contraction	50	Änggård and Berg-ström, 1963
$F_{2\alpha}$		Spontaneous contraction	10–50	Bergström *et al.*, 1959b
	Stilbestrol	Spontaneous contraction	1	Änggård and Berg-ström, 1963
	Stilbestrol	Spontaneous contraction	25–50	Horton and Main, 1965b
	Estradiol	Electrical stimulation	0.5–1	Sullivan, 1966

sible that the exact hormonal status plays a role since Änggård and Bergström (1963) reported that stilbestrol treatment increased the sensitivity of the uterus 10–50 times. The difference in results reported by Horton and Main (1963, 1965b) with respect to the threshold doses and relative activities for PGE_1 and $PGF_{2\alpha}$ also supports the idea that the exact hormonal status may be of importance. From Table 4.VII one would calculate the ratio $PGF_{2\alpha}/PGE_1$ to be about 0.4–0.9, but the observed ratio was 8 (5–15) (Table 4.VIII). On the other hand, Pickles *et al.* (1966) and Sullivan (1966) did not find the hormonal status of the rat or addition of progesterone to the bath fluid to have any specific effect on the response of the isolated rat uterus to prostaglandins.

The rat uterus often shows a marked tachyphylaxis to PGE_1 and $PGF_{1\alpha}$, but less often to PGE_2 and rarely to total prostaglandin extracts (Fig. 4.27). There is no cross desensitization between E_1, E_2, and $F_{1\alpha}$, as illustrated in Figs. 4.28 and 4.29 (Eliasson, 1959; Adamson *et al.*, 1967). The reason why such a tachyphylaxis occurs for PGE_1 and $PGF_{1\alpha}$ but not for the partially purified prosta-

TABLE 4.VIII
ACTIVITY RATIOS (MEAN VALUES) BETWEEN DIFFERENT PROSTAGLANDINS
WHEN TESTED ON ISOLATED RAT UTERUS

Prosta-glandins	Hormonal status or treatment	Method	Activity ratio	References
$E_2 : E_1$	Stilbestrol	Spontaneous contraction	1.1	Horton and Main, 1963
$E_3 : E_1$	Stilbestrol	Spontaneous contraction	0.3	Horton and Main, 1963
$F_{1\alpha} : E_1$	Stilbestrol	Spontaneous contraction	0.9	Horton and Main, 1963
$F_{1\alpha} : E_1$	Stilbestrol	Spontaneous contraction	3	Bergström et al., 1959b
$F_{1\alpha} : E_1$	Estradiol	Spontaneous contraction	1	Adamson et al., 1967
$F_{1\alpha} : F_{1\beta}$	Stilbestrol	Spontaneous contraction	24	Horton and Main, 1966a
$F_{2\alpha} : E_1$	Stilbestrol	Spontaneous contraction	8	Horton and Main, 1965b
$F_{2\alpha} : E_1$	Estradiol	Electrical stimulation	5	Sullivan, 1966
$F_{2\alpha} : F_{1\alpha}$		Spontaneous contraction	1–5	Änggård and Berg-ström, 1963
Nor-$E_1 : E_1$		Spontaneous contraction	1	Horton and Main, 1966a

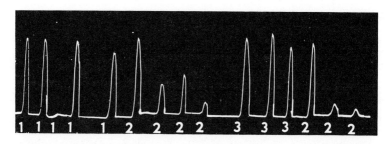

FIG. 4.27. Effects of various prostaglandin preparations on isolated rat uterus. Bath volume, 3 ml. Temperature, 30°C. Peaks marked 1 = prostaglandin extracted from sheep semen equivalent to 0.085 ml; 2 = 10 μg of PGE_1; 3 = prostaglandin extracted from incubated vesicular glands of sheep equivalent to 20 mg of tissue (after Eliasson, 1959). Note the tachyphylaxis for PGE_1.

glandin from sheep seminal fluid of sheep vesicular glands is not clear. The decrease in sensitivity is more marked for PGE_1 than for $PGF_{1\alpha}$. The fact that the rat uterus, after being partially desensitized to one prostaglandin (e.g., PGE_1), still gives a normal or potentiated response to another prostaglandin (e.g., $PGF_{1\alpha}$ or PGE_2) strongly indicates the presence of different receptors (cf. Pickles, 1967).

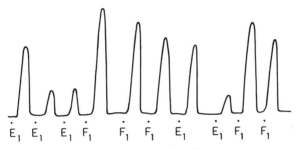

FIG. 4.28. Tachyphylactic response in isolated rat uterus to prostaglandins E and $F_{1\alpha}$. Bath volume, 5 ml. Temperature, 30°C. $E_1 = 0.8$ μg of PGE_1/ml and $F_{1\alpha} = 1.2$ μg of $PGF_{1\alpha}$/ml. Note that tachyphylaxis for one prostaglandin does not decrease the response for the other compound (after Adamson *et al.*, 1967).

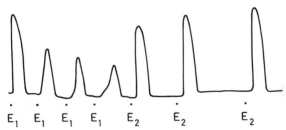

FIG. 4.29. This experiment demonstrates that an isolated rat uterus can show a marked tachyphylactic response to PGE_1 (0.0 μg/ml) without having the same reactivity pattern for PGE_2 (1.2 μg/ml) (after Adamson *et al.*, 1967).

The intact rat uterus is highly insensitive to partly purified prostaglandin from human semen (Eliasson, 1959).

Prostaglandin E_1 (1–5 μg/ml or 10–30 μg/kg) has no effect on the motility of the rat vas deferens. It was further reported by Mantegazza and Naimzada (1965) that there is no interaction with the motility caused by electrical stimulation of the hypogastric nerves or catecholamine administration. Clegg (1966a) likewise found PGE_1 (5 μg/ml) without direct effect on the motility, but reported adrenaline-induced contractions to be inhibited even at a dose of 1 ng of PGE/ml.

C. Cardiovascular System

One of the characteristics of the crude prostaglandin extract is that it lowers the blood pressure after intravenous injection in the rabbit, cat, and dog. Experiments with the crystalline prostaglandins have usually shown the PGE's to be rather more active than the PGF's. However, marked quantitative and qualitative differences occur between species as well as between various parts of the cardiovascular system.

1. CARDIOVASCULAR RESPONSES

a. Man

Reddening of the face and feelings of warmth and oppression in the head and chest are the general symptoms following intravenous infusion of PGE_1 (0.1–0.7 μg/kg/minute). The symptoms are more pronounced at the higher dose levels and persist some 5–10 minutes after the end of the infusion. In one subject, infusion of 0.1–0.2 μg of PGE_1/kg/minute into the distal part of the left subclavian artery produced intense flush in the left arm and, within 10 minutes, also produced edema in the left hand (Bergström et al., 1959a, 1965a,b).

The cardiovascular response to an intravenous infusion of PGE_1 (0.1–0.7 μg/kg/minute) was first tachycardia; the increase in pulse rate was of the order of 20%. At higher dose levels, there was also a fall in the systolic and diastolic pressures, as illustrated in Fig. 4.30 (see also Table 4.IX). The pressures in the right ventricle and the pulmonary capillary vein pressure (PCV, measured with the tip of the catheter in the wedge position) were unchanged, but a slight tendency toward elevation of the pressure in the pulmonary artery was observed. The cardiac output decreased about 20%. The results indicated that PGE_1 causes an increase in the pulmonary vascular resistance (Bergström et al., 1959a, 1965a,b).

The effect of PGE₂, PGE₃, and the PGF's on the human cardiovascular system is so far unreported. Injection of PGA₂ (50 μg)
into a patient with hypertension caused a moderate and short-
lasting lowering of the blood pressure (Lee, 1967).

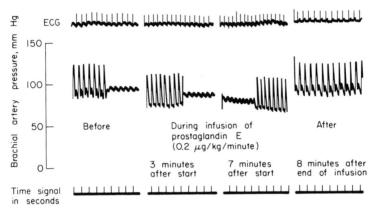

FIG. 4.30. Effect of intravenous infusion of PGE₁ (0.2 μg/kg/minute) on the
pulse rate and arterial blood pressure in a healthy young male. ECG = electro-
cardiogram. Records before and various times after the start and end of infusion (after Bergström *et al.*, 1959a).

b. Dog

A fall in blood pressure and an increase in heart rate follows
the intravascular infusion of PGE₁ (Steinberg *et al.*, 1963; Carlson and Orö, 1966; Carlson, 1967). The effect is, however, dependent upon the mode of administration; infusion of PGE₁ high
in the aorta has a more pronounced action than infusion low in
the aorta or intravenously (Fig. 4.31). The increase in heart rate
could be counteracted by a sympathetic ganglion-blocking agent
or by pretreatment with reserpine. Blocking of the sympathetic
β-receptors did not change the blood pressure response to injected PGE₁, but markedly reduced the effect on the heart rate
(Carlson and Orö, 1966). Similar results were obtained by Mc-
Curdy and Nakano (1966), who in addition registered a decrease
in the atrial pressures whereas pulmonary arterial pressure,
cardiac output, and myocardial contractile force increased in
proportion to the dose given. No apparent evidence of tachyphylaxis was noted.

TABLE 4.IX

PULSE RATE, BLOOD PRESSURE, CARDIAC OUTPUT, AND STROKE VOLUME BEFORE, DURING AND AFTER INFUSION OF PROSTAGLANDIN E_1 (PGE₁) IN A SINGLE EXPERIMENT[a]

	Pulse rate	Right ventricle (mm Hg)		Pulmonary artery (mm Hg)			PCV (mm Hg)	Brachial artery (mm Hg)			Cardiac output (liter/minute)	Stroke volume (ml)
		Systolic	End diastolic	Systolic	Diastolic	Mean	Mean	Systolic	Diastolic	Mean		
Resting value before PGE (minutes)	80	18	1	19	4	7	8	137	86	105	10.1	126
											10.3	128
Infusion of PGE, 15 µg per min 1.5	84	18	1				7	127	83	97		
3	94	17	1					121	77	94	8.4	90
5	94	19	1	18	4	6	7	119	72	88		
7	104	21	0					112	55	85		
After infusion of PGE 3	97	20	0	18	4	7		121	75	102		
8	92							130	88	105		

[a] After Bergström et al. (1959a).

An interesting observation was made by Carlson and Orö (1966) that infusion of PGE₁ into dog common carotid artery in most experiments increased the systemic arterial blood pressure. The reaction could be abolished or reversed by pretreating the animals with a sympathetic ganglion-blocking agent; this suggests that PGE₁ could stimulate sympathetic vasoconstrictor activity either through an effect on the carotid sinus or on the central nervous system.

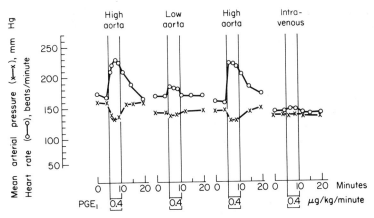

FIG. 4.31. Effect of infusions of PGE₁ by various routes on blood pressure and heart rate in an experiment on an anesthetized dog. PGE₁ was administered in the following order: high in aorta, low in aorta, high in aorta, and intravenously, as indicated (after Carlson and Orö, 1966).

According to Bergström *et al.* (1967), the infusion of PGA₁ has a similar but more pronounced effect than PGE₁ on the blood pressure and heart rate.

Intravenous infusion of PGE₂ into trained, unanesthetized dogs causes a fall in systemic blood pressure and an increase in heart rate (DuCharme and Weeks, 1967).

Trained, unanesthetized dogs respond to intravenous injection of PGF₂α with rises in the systemic blood pressure, in the right auricular pressure, and in the cardiac output. This reactivity pattern differs from that after injection of other hypertensive agents (e.g., angiotensin) that tend to leave the cardiac output unchanged or decreased. There was no concomitant change in myocardial contractile force. A more detailed analysis of the action of $PGF_{2\alpha}$ on the cardiovascular system of dog revealed that this compound was a most active venoconstrictor agent, particularly on the small peripheral veins (see below) (DuCharme and Weeks, 1967).

Removal of the kidneys from the dog is, under certain conditions, associated with hypertension. This increase in blood pressure can, according to Muirhead *et al.* (1967), be counteracted by daily injections of PGE_1 (15–29 μg/kg/day), PGA_1 (50–100 μg/kg/day), or $PGF_{1\alpha}$ (15–30 μg/kg/day). The mechanism of action has not yet been clarified.

c. Rabbit

Intravenous infusions of PGE_1, PGE_2, and PGE_3 lower the arterial blood pressure and concomitantly increase the heart rate, as shown in Fig. 4.32. The activity is highest for E_1 and lowest for

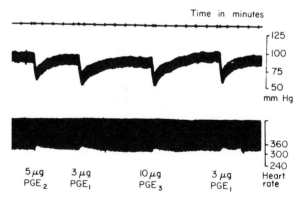

FIG. 4.32. Effect of intravenous injection of prostaglandins E_1, E_2, and E_3 on the rabbit arterial blood pressure (after Bergström and von Euler, 1963).

E_3. Nor-PGE_1 is only one-tenth as active as PGE_1. $PGF_{1\alpha}$ is also hypotensive, but about 10–20 times less active than E_1. The activity ratio in rabbit blood pressure between $PGF_{1\alpha}$ and $PGF_{1\beta}$ is greater than 5 (Bergström *et al.*, 1959b; Bergström and von

Euler, 1963; Horton and Main, 1963, 1966a). Intravenous administration of $PGF_{2\alpha}$ causes a lowering of the blood pressure, but without affecting the right ventricular pressure or heart rate (Änggård and Bergström, 1963; Horton and Main, 1965b).

Injection of 1–50 μg of PGE_1 into the pulmonary artery causes a vasodilation in the vascular bed of the isolated rabbit lung preparation. The average vasodilatating effect was about the same as that of adrenaline. Inhibitors of the adrenergic α- and β-receptors with phentolamine and propranolol, respectively, did not alter the response to PGE_1 (Hauge et al., 1967). Using a purified extract of sheep vesicular gland, von Euler (1939) observed a vasoconstrictor effect on the isolated rabbit lung.

d. Cat

Intravenous injection of a prostaglandin extract from sheep vesicular glands causes a fall in the arterial blood pressure, but not if the cat has been eviscerated (von Euler, 1939). This and other experiments suggested that vasoconstriction in the portal circulation is of importance for the hypotensive effect. If prostaglandin is injected intraarterially in the cat, it causes a slight fall in the systemic blood pressure after about 15 seconds, followed by a more pronounced lowering of the pressure. The initial response apparently owed to a weak local vasodilation.

Prostaglandin E_1 likewise causes a lowering of the blood pressure and tachycardia when injected in doses of 1–3 μg/kg (Main, 1964).

Intravenous injection in the cat of 15–30 μg of $PGF_{2\alpha}$/kg lowers the systolic blood pressure, but, in contrast to the rabbit, there is also an elevation of the right ventricular pressure. Sometimes these changes are associated with a marked bradycardia. The decrease in heart rate is most likely of reflex origin, since there is a delayed onset of 10–30 seconds and the effect can be counteracted by vagotomy or atropine (Fig. 4.33). Injection of $PGF_{2\alpha}$ into the aorta caused only a small reduction in systemic blood pressure (Änggård and Bergström, 1963).

Hauge et al. (1967) found PGE_1 to cause less vasodilatation in the isolated cat lung preparation than in rabbit lungs. The cat heart–lung preparation was also less sensitive to a sheep vesicular gland extract (von Euler, 1939).

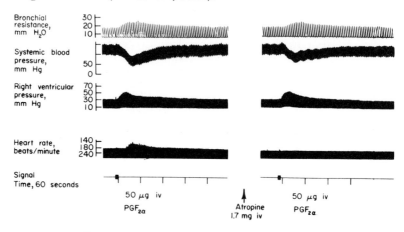

FIG. 4.33. Effects of intravenous injection of $PGF_{2\alpha}$ in a cat before and after atropine. Note that the bradycardia occurs after about 20 seconds latency and is abolished by atropine (after Änggård and Bergström, 1963).

e. Other Species

$PGF_{2\alpha}$ is a pressure agent in the anesthetized pentolinium-blocked rat, but PGE_1 causes a fall in blood pressure (Table 4.X). Reserpine pretreatment did not change the response (DuCharme and Weeks, 1967). Also in the spinal chick, $PGF_{2\alpha}$ is hypertensive in action (Horton and Main, 1965a, 1967).

In contrast to other test systems, the guinea pig blood pressure is more sensitive to dihydro-PGE_1 than to PGE_1. The following activities for three metabolites in relation to PGE_1 (= 1) were observed: dihydro-PGE, 1.6:1; 15-keto-PGE, 0.02:1; and 15-ketodihydro-PGE_1 <0.01:1 (Änggård, 1966b).

2. PERIPHERAL BLOOD FLOW

Intraarterial injections of PGE_1 in dogs increase the blood flow in coronary, brachial, femoral, carotid, and renal arteries (McCurdy and Nakano, 1966).

TABLE 4.X

EFFECT OF GANGLION BLOCKADE AND ANESTHESIA ON BLOOD PRESSURE
RESPONSE TO PGE₁, ANGIOTENSIN, AND PGF₂α IN THE RAT[a]

Compound	Blood pressure of unanesthetized and unrestrained rats (mm Hg)		Blood pressure of unrestrained rats after pentolinium (10 mg/kg iv)		Blood pressure of rats after sodium pentobarbital (30 mg/kg iv) and pentolinium	
	Initial	Change ± SEM	Initial	Change ± SEM	Initial	Change ± SEM
Prostaglandin E₁, 10 μg/kg iv	111	−24±2.2	60	−17±1.5	58	−20±1.8
Angiotensin II, 0.05 μg/kg iv	108	+13±1.4	64	+24±3.1	58	+20±2.9
Prostaglandin F₂α, 10 μg/kg iv	106	+10±2.2	61	+22±3.4	62	+18±3.5

[a] After DuCharme and Weeks (1967). Each figure is a mean for six rats.

Prostaglandin $F_{2\alpha}$ is an active venoconstrictor agent in the dog. The action is dependent on an intact innervation, since, for example, denervation of a hind limb abolishes the effect. Electrical stimulation of the peripheral part of the cut nerves can, however, restore the reactivity, and effects of prostaglandin $F_{2\alpha}$ on the minor veins could be modified by changing the frequency of the nerve stimulation (DuCharme and Weeks, 1967). PGA_2 is vasodilator in action (Lee, 1967).

In the anesthetized cat, close arterial injection of the PGE's causes an increase in the gastrocnemius-muscle blood flow (Fig. 4.34) and in hind-limb-skin blood flow. The threshold doses for PGE_1 are about 0.5 and 0.1 μg/kg, respectively. The activity ratio between E_1, E_2, E_3, and $F_{1\alpha}$ is about $1:0.8:0.5:0.2$ for gastrocnemius-muscle blood flow and $1:0.9:0.2:0.2$ for hind-limb-skin blood flow (Horton, 1963; Horton and Main, 1963). The number of experiments are, however, still very limited and the figures therefore approximate. It is possible that the increase in muscle blood flow is related to an interaction with the sympathetic neurotransmittor (cf. Section 4,F).

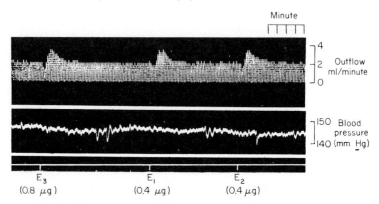

FIG. 4.34. Effect of close arterial injection of prostaglandins E_1, E_2, and E_3 on venous outflow from cat gastrocnemius muscle and arterial blood pressure (after Horton and Main, 1963).

Intraarterial injection of 1–10 μg of $PGF_{2\alpha}$ into the femoral artery of the skinned hind leg, the superior mesenteric artery, or the renal artery of the cat increased the blood flow only through the muscles (Änggård and Bergström, 1963; Horton and Main, 1965b).

A total prostaglandin extract from human semen regularly dilated the vessels of the perfused frog hind-limb (von Euler, 1936).

On the human placenta a purified extract of sheep vesicular gland caused strong vasoconstriction (von Euler, 1938).

3. ISOLATED HEART

Prostaglandin E_1 in doses of 0.01–1.0 μg/ml of perfusion fluid has a marked and usually long-lasting positive inotropic and chronotropic effect on the isolated guinea pig heart prepared according to Langendorff (Fig. 4.35). In the same dose range, there is no such effect on the isolated hearts from the rabbit, cat, or rat (Berti *et al.*, 1965; Mantegazza, 1965; Vergroesen *et al.*, 1967). These results are in keeping with von Euler's (1936, 1939) observation that prostaglandin extracts from human semen or sheep vesicular glands had no effect on isolated rabbit heart prepared according to Langendorff.

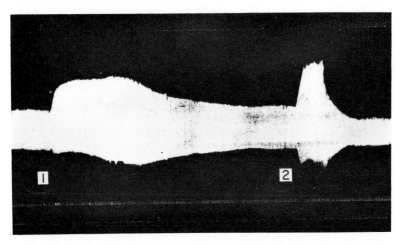

FIG. 4.35. Effect of PGE$_1$ on the contractions and coronary flow of the isolated guinea pig heart perfused according to Langendorff. Bottom curve, time in minutes. Point 1 = 1 μg of PGE$_1$ in 0.1 ml of solvent; 2 = 1 μg of adrenaline in 0.1 ml of solvent (after Berti *et al.*, 1965).

In high doses, PGE$_1$ had a negative inotropic effect on the rabbit heart (75 μg) and a positive inotropic effect on the rat heart (10 μg) (Berti *et al.*, 1965).

In the isolated perfused heart from cat, rabbit, guinea pig, or rat, PGE$_1$ causes an increase in the coronary flow. At a dose level of 1 μg/ml, the increase can be about 250% in the rat heart. A marked tachyphylaxis was, however, noted in rat heart (Berti *et al.*, 1965; Mantegazza, 1965; Vergroesen *et al.*, 1967).

PGF$_{1\alpha}$ in doses of 1 μg/ml markedly increased the contraction force of the rat heart, although PGF$_{1\beta}$ was much less active. The two PGF compounds did not affect the heart or coronary perfusion rate (Vergroesen *et al.*, 1967). The same authors also investigated several isomers and analogs of PGE$_1$ and E$_2$ with 18, 19, 20, 21, and 22 carbon atoms. They were all without any effect on the isolated rat heart.

The action of human semen prostaglandin extract on the frog heart (Straub preparation) was characterized by an increase in heart rate and contractile force with incomplete diastolic relaxation (von Euler, 1936). Berti *et al.* (1965) reported that addition of 1 μg of PGE$_1$ to the perfusion fluid for the isolated frog heart elicited a long-lasting positive inotropic effect.

4. CAPILLARY PERMEABILITY

Bergström *et al.* (1965a) reported that infusion of PGE$_1$ into the left subclavian artery of a man caused marked edema in the left hand.

Intradermal injection of PGE$_1$ (1 μg in 0.1 ml) in guinea pigs pretreated with Pontamine sky blue increased the capillary permeability. In comparison with bradykinin, prostaglandin E$_1$ was at least 10–100 times less active (Horton, 1963).

D. Nervous System

1. CENTRAL NERVOUS SYSTEM

As further mentioned in Chapters 3 and 6, extracts with prostaglandin-like behavior have been prepared from the central nervous system of various animals. These findings, together with our knowledge of the release of such substances as a result of various kinds of stimulation, seem to support the significance of the effects observed on the nervous system after administration of prostaglandins.

The first indications of prostaglandin activity on the central nervous system stem from Horton (1964), who observed that certain compounds belonging to the E series produced stupor and prolonged sedation when injected into the cerebral ventricles of cats, and sedation upon intravenous injection into chicks. These experiments were later extended (Horton and Main, 1965a,c).

a. Cat

The intraventricular injections in the cat were made through a Collison cannula implanted in the lateral ventricle according to the method of Feldberg and Sherwood (1953). Injections were made after the cannula had been implanted for 1 week in the unanesthetized animal. The doses used were 3–60 μg/kg of PGE_1 in neutral solution of 0.1–0.2 ml in volume. Within 5–20 minutes after doses of 7–20 μg/kg, the animals showed sedation and stupor in a characteristic posture with head forward and slightly lowered. No impairment of the movements was observed when the cat was temporarily alerted. The cat reacted sluggishly to some stimuli, but always silently. In some cases, after a latency of 40 minutes or more, there were signs of catatonia; thus, animals would remain immobile when placed in unusual and uncomfortable positions for as long as 90 minutes (Fig. 4.36). The catatonic signs lasted up to 4 hours and the sedation and lack of spontaneity remained for 24–48 hours. The threshold dose for

FIG. 4.36. Cat 1 hour after an injection into the cerebral ventricles of 20 μg of prostaglandin E_1 (after Horton and Main, 1965c).

the sedative effect was 3 μg of PGE/kg and lasted for 4–8 hours. Pupillary dilation was also observed, but no other signs of stimulation. Intravenous injections of PGE_1 also caused sedation, although larger doses, 30 μg/kg, were necessary to produce the effect.

Comparative studies were also made with other PG compounds. PGE_2 and PGE_3 were somewhat less active; 12 μg/kg had about the same effect as 7 μg/kg of PGE_1.

$PGF_{2\alpha}$, on the other hand, did not cause any obvious symptoms when injected in the cerebral ventricles in doses equal to or higher than those of PGE_1 that caused catatonia and stupor (Horton and Main, 1965c). From these observations it also follows that the symptoms caused by E_1 are not nonspecific effects of long-chain fatty acids, but rather represent a significant biological effect. The occurrence of the inactive $PGF_{2\alpha}$ in the brain (Samuelsson, 1964b) is perhaps somewhat puzzling in this connection, since it is the only compound of this series that has so far been found in brain tissue. The possibility of a transformation from E_1 to $F_{2\alpha}$ in the brain should not be discounted, however, and according to Ramwell and Shaw (1964), PGE_1 or PGE_2 are released from the cerebral cortex into a superfusate as a result of afferent or cortical stimulation.

The effect of prostaglandins has also been tested on cortical neurons in the cat. Krnjević (1965) did not observe any definite effects of PGE_1 on 18 cortical neurons in two cats. On the other hand, Avanzino et al. (1966) found a marked stimulating action of PGE_1 on brain-stem neurons. In these experiments, PGE_1 was administered by iontophoresis through multibarrelled micropipettes inserted into the medulla of unanesthetized, decerebrated cats. Most of the neurons were located in the medial reticular formation of the medulla. Of the 121 neurons studied, 50 (41%) were excited and 71 (59%) gave no response when PGE_1 was applied. Repeated application of PGE_1 caused a progressive reduction in the effect with some neurons, but others showed no change in response. Excitation of neurons was observed with PGE_1, PGE_2, and $PGF_{2\alpha}$. Figure 4.37 shows an activating effect of PGE_1 and $PGF_{2\alpha}$ on a neuron in the nucleus reticularis gigantocellularis, which fired only occasionally during rest. Inhibitory effects were also observed with E_1 and $F_{2\alpha}$ (Fig. 4.38), but not with E_2 (Avanzino et al., 1966, 1967). The figure shows in addition a specific desensitization for E_1 and $F_{2\alpha}$, but no cross tachyphylaxis (cf. Chapter 4, Section B,3,d).

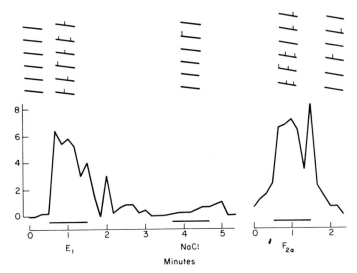

FIG. 4.37. The effect of PGE_1 and $PGF_{2\alpha}$ on the impulse frequency of a neuron in the nucleus reticularis gigantocellularis of the cat. E_1 and $F_{2\alpha}$ were applied by iontophoresis with 100 nA for 30 seconds. Above the graph are shown corresponding records of the neuron potentials, photographed from oscilloscope sweeps of 200 msec duration, triggered every 1 second. Ordinate impulses per second (after Avanzino *et al.*, 1966).

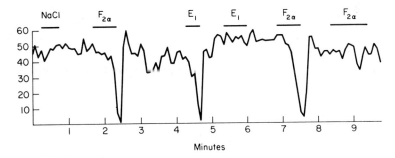

FIG. 4.38. Effects of E_1 (100 nA) and $F_{2\alpha}$ (100 nA) on the impulse frequency of a neuron in the nucleus reticularis gigantocellularis of the cat. Desensitization occurred with repeat doses (after Avanzino *et al.*, 1966).

b. Chick

Marked effects were noted in the chick, which is thought to lack a blood–brain barrier. Thus prostaglandins E_1, E_2, and E_3 were all active in doses as low as 1 μg intravenously, causing sedation, loss of spontaneous activity, and closure of the eyes. In higher doses, the compounds caused loss of righting reflexes (Horton, 1964). Interestingly, $PGF_{2\alpha}$ caused no sedation, but an extension or abduction of the legs (Fig. 4.39). An analysis of this effect showed that it owed to a stimulating action on the spinal cord (Horton and Main, 1965a). Prostaglandin $F_{2\alpha}$ had no effect on the contractions of the gastrocnemius muscle elicited by ipsilateral sciatic stimulation in the spinal chick, but strongly increased the response to contralateral stimulation (Fig. 4.40). The effect of PGE_1 was similar to that of $PGF_{2\alpha}$ on this preparation, which is of interest since E_1 does not produce increased muscle tension in the chloralosed or unanesthetized chick.

FIG. 4.39. Chick (40 gm) 1 minute after an intravenous injection of 4 μg of prostaglandin $F_{2\alpha}$ (after Horton and Main, 1965c).

Nor-PGE₁ like PGE₁ caused sedation and potentiation of the crossed extensor reflex in the chick, but had only about one-tenth the activity of PGE₁.

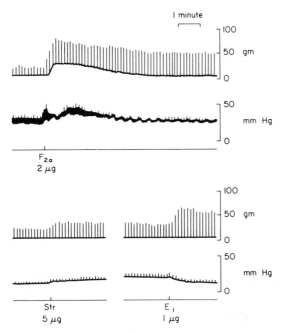

FIG. 4.40. Spinal chick. Upper trace: gastrocnemius muscle tension recorded isometrically. Lower trace: arterial blood pressure. Reflex contractions of gastrocnemius muscle were elicited by 5-V pulses of 25 msec duration. $F_{2\alpha}$ = prostaglandin $F_{2\alpha}$; E_1 = prostaglandin E_1, and Str = strychnine hydrochloride; all injections were made into the right external jugular vein (after Horton and Main, 1965a).

c. Mouse

Intravenous injection of PGE₁ also caused transient sedation and some decrease in spontaneous activity in mice.

2. PERIPHERAL NERVOUS SYSTEM

As mentioned above, Horton (1965) has suggested that part of the stimulating action of PGE₁ on the isolated guinea pig ileum is mediated by a nervous pathway, since the effect is partially counteracted by atropine. No indications have so far been obtained that prostaglandins should affect the neuromuscular transmission process in the superior cervical ganglion

Although evidence for actions of prostaglandins on peripheral nervous mechanisms is only very slight, it may be recalled that release of prostaglandins as a result of nerve stimulation has been reported for a variety of organs and tissues (diaphragm, epididymal fat pad, adrenal medulla, spleen), as mentioned in Chapter 3. Of particular interest is that release of prostaglandins from nervous structures has also been observed in the frog, indicating that these compounds have a wide distribution in the animal kingdom.

E. Metabolic Effects

1. ACTION ON LIPOLYSIS IN VITRO

It has been shown by Steinberg *et al.* (1963) that PGE_1 counteracts the effect of adrenaline and noradrenaline and other agents, such as ACTH and glucagon, on the fat breakdown in rat epididymal fat pads *in vitro*. Thus the release of glycerol and fatty acids into the medium is inhibited by the presence of PGE_1 in concentrations of 20 ng/ml or more.

Further studies (Steinberg *et al.*, 1964) showed that PGE_1 was more active than PGE_2 and PGE_3 in counteracting the hormone-induced lipolytic effect and also more efficient than $PGF_{1\alpha}$ and $PGF_{2\alpha}$. No action was observed with $PGF_{1\beta}$ in 5 μg/ml. The actions of PGE_1 on various activators of lipolysis are shown in Fig. 4.41 (Steinberg and Vaughan, 1967). PGE_1 also inhibited the hormone-stimulated activation of phosphorylase, although this effect appeared to be smaller than that on the lipase. The adrenaline stimulation of glucose release did not seem to be influenced by PGE_1. In these experiments it was also shown that PGE_1 alone significantly reduced the basal glycerol release from adipose tissue in a concentration of 0.1 μg/ml.

An analysis of the mechanism of action of PGE_1 on the lipolytic system led Steinberg and Vaughan (1967) to the conclusion that PGE_1 exerts its antilipolytic activity by interfering with the formation of cyclic adenosine 5-phosphate and not with the later steps by which this compound induces lipase activation. The results of Butcher *et al.* (1967) and of Orloff *et al.* (1965) support this conclusion.

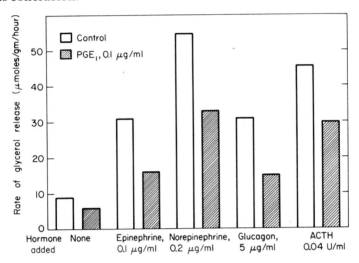

FIG. 4.41. Effect of PGE_1 on the rate of basal glycerol release from adipose tissue and after hormone-induced stimulation (after Steinberg and Vaughan, 1967).

Steinberg and Vaughan (1967) also discuss a problem of more general scope regarding the action of PGE_1, in that they consider the possibility that prostaglandins exert a counterhormonal activity in the basal state.

It has later been shown that the inhibitory effect of PGE_1 on the free fatty acid (FFA) and glycerol release from epididymal adipose tissue is smaller in essential fatty acid- (EFA) deficient rats than in controls (Bergström and Carlson, 1965a). Thus in the controls 0.1 μg/ml of noradrenaline caused an increase in the release of FFA from 0.85 ± 0.15 μmoles/gm/hour to 4.78 ± 0.41, which was reduced to 1.06 ± 0.12 with 1 μg/ml of PGE_1. In the deficient rats the basal figure was higher, 1.91 ± 0.20 μmoles/gm/hour, increased to 4.76 ± 0.32 after treatment with noradrenaline, and was reduced to 1.64 ± 0.18 after treatment with PGE_1. Analogous effects were observed for glycerol, although PGE$_1$ caused a marked reduction of the initial value in the controls.

Bergström and Carlson (1965b) studied the effect of PGE$_1$ on human subcutaneous adipose tissue *in vitro*. On this material PGE$_1$ consistently inhibited the basal release of glycerol and FFA and also the releasing effect of noradrenaline (Table 4.XI).

Various factors influence the antilipolytic effect of PGE$_1$. Thus its effect is more marked in hyperthyroid rats (Paoletti *et al.*, 1967). The same authors also noted that the lipolytic activity of noradrenaline and theophylline on adipose tissue was greater in rats deficient in essential fatty acids, in agreement with the results of Bergström and Carlson (1965a).

TABLE 4.XI

THE EFFECT OF PGE$_1$ ON THE RELEASE OF GLYCEROL (μ MOLES/GM/HOUR) FROM HUMAN SUBCUTANEOUS ADIPOSE TISSUE (FROM FIVE PATIENTS) INCUBATED *in Vitro* IN A KREBS-RINGER BICARBONATE BUFFER CONTAINING 2% HUMAN ALBUMIN AND 0.1% GLUCOSE[a,b]

Exp. No.	Amount of PGE$_1$ added (μg/ml)				
	0	0.001	0.01	0.1	1
9	0.63±0.06	–	0.44±0.05	0.34±0.05	–
	(5)		(5)	(5)	
10	0.55±0.05	0.58±0.06	0.45±0.05	0.35±0.03	0.33±0.04

[a] Mean value ± standard error of the mean. Values within parentheses indicate number of incubation flasks.
[b] After Carlson (1965).

In low concentrations, PGE$_1$ reduced glycerol release from the adipose tissue of fed rats, but the action was absent in fasted rats (Carlson, 1966, 1967) (Fig. 4.42).

The importance of the nutritional state is also borne out by the results of Stock and Westermann (1966). Thus PGE$_1$ in a concentration of 2.5 μg/ml inhibited the release of glycerol from isolated fat pads of normal rats as well as the increased release in alloxan-diabetic animals, but had no action on the increased release from adipose tissue in fasting animals.

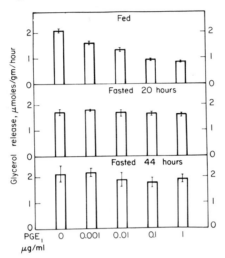

FIG. 4.42. Effect of various concentration of PGE_1 on the release of glycerol from epididymal adipose tissue of fed and fasted rats incubated *in vitro*. Mean ± SEM (after Carlson, 1966).

2. ACTION ON LIPOLYSIS *In Vivo*

Bergström *et al.* (1964c) showed that the prostaglandins E_1, E_2, and E_3 also inhibit the catecholamine-induced lipolysis *in vivo* on anesthetized dogs. $PGF_{1\alpha}$ was inactive in this respect when applied in similar doses. As seen in Fig. 4.43 the effect of PGE_1 on the FFA is well marked both when infused intravenously in a dose of 0.4 μg/kg/minute and particularly when given intraarterially, which causes a long-lasting effect. Single injections of 5–10 μg of prostaglandins E_1, E_2, and E_3 during a continuous infusion of noradrenaline caused a temporary decrease in the free fatty acids present in plasma; this was less marked for E_3 and absent for PGF_1 (Fig. 4.44). PGE_1 also blocks the effect of adrenaline and isoprenaline. The turnover rate of FFA before infusion of PGE_1 in a dose of 0.4 μg/kg/minute was 0.1 nmole/minute. After 90 minutes of infusion of noradrenaline, 0.5 μg/kg/

minute, it had increased to 0.7 nmoles/minute and fell during the infusion of PGE₁ to 0.05–0.1 nmole/minute. The plasma glycerol concentration increased about 5-fold during noradrenaline infusion and fell immediately when PGE₁ was given.

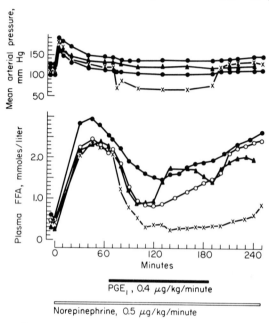

FIG. 4.43. Effect of intravenous (●, ○, Δ) infusion in three dogs and intra-arterial (x) infusion in one dog of PGE₁ during infusion of norepinephrine (after Bergström *et al.*, 1964c).

Injection of PGE₁ alone in human subjects, on the other hand, caused an increase in heart rate and raised the concentration of FFA and glycerol in plasma, when given either intravenously or intra-arterially in a dose of 0.1 μg/kg/minute (Bergström *et al.*, 1965a,b). Although PGE₁ diminished or eliminated the increased blood pressure and bradycardia caused by noradrenaline, it had only little effect on the noradrenaline-induced increase in FFA and glycerol in plasma (Fig. 4.45).

Studies on the effects of PGE₁ on the FFA and glycerol concentration in the plasma of dogs showed that both of these were raised in the nonanesthetized dog and in 9 out of 12 anesthetized dogs, while the FFA level decreased in 3 dogs (Bergström *et al.*, 1966a). Injections were made intravenously in the first case and high in the aorta in the anesthetized dogs. Intravenous or intra-carotidal infusion also raised the FFA level in anesthetized dogs. Studies of the turnover rate of plasma FFA showed that the effects observed owed entirely to changes in the rate of mobilization of FFA into blood plasma. The concentrations of glycerol followed the same pattern as the FFA.

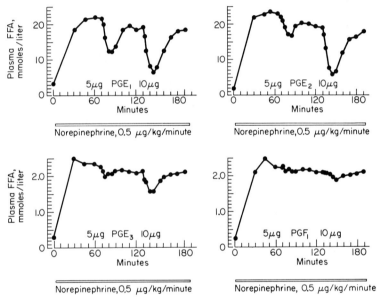

FIG. 4.44. Effect of intravenous injections of PGE₁, PGE₂, PGE₃, and PGF₁ₐ on the arterial FFA levels during continuous infusion of noradrenaline into anesthetized dogs (after Bergström *et al.*, 1964c).

In addition to the effects on catecholamine-induced lipolysis, PGE₁ prevents the rise in plasma FFA caused by dimethylphenylpiperazinium bromide (DMPP), which acts as a nicotine-like ganglion-stimulating agent.

From these experiments it emerges that PGE₁ may induce a rise in FFA and glycerol in plasma both in anesthetized and un-

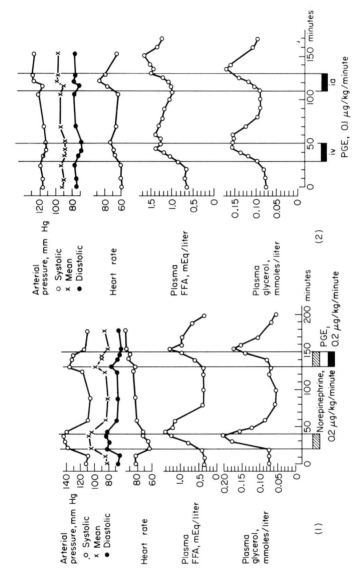

Fig. 4.45. (1) Blood pressure, heart rate, and arterial concentration of FFA and glycerol in plasma during intravenous infusion of norepinephrine and during simultaneous intravenous infusions of norepinephrine and PGE₁. (2) Blood pressure, heart rate, and arterial concentration of FFA and glycerol in plasma during infusions of PGE₁ in another subject. The first infusion of PGE₁ was given intravenously, the second intraarterially in the aortic arch (after Bergström et al., 1965b).

anesthetized dogs *in vivo* as it does in man. On the other hand, PGE_1 inhibits the rise in plasma FFA and glycerol caused by noradrenaline and other sympathomimetic amines and gangli- onic stimulatory agents, which suggests that the "true" effect of PGE_1 is an inhibitory one on the lipolysis. This would also be in harmony with the effects observed *in vitro*, in which PGE_1 consistently inhibited the release of FFA and glycerol.

A stimulating effect on the adrenergic or adrenomedullary system possibly mediated by the barosensitive or chemosensi- tive reflex areas of the carotid artery or aorta may be considered as a cause of the stimulatory effect of PGE_1 on lipolysis. It would be of interest to observe whether or not the effect remains after denervation of these areas. Another possibility is that PGE_1 in low concentrations exerts a central stimulatory action of adrener- gic mechanisms (Carlson and Orö, 1966), perhaps on hypothala- mic metabolic centers, leading to increased release and activity of the catecholamines. The apparently contradictory inhibitory effects of PGE_1 on the FFA raising action of catecholamines and DMPP may be explained by the concentrations of PGE_1 acting on the tissues. If these are sufficiently high, as in the experiments with infusion of 0.25–0.8 µg/kg/minute, the direct inhibitory effect on the issue itself may account for the abolition of action (Bergström *et al.*, 1966b).

The same authors have further studied the effect of infusions of PGE_1 alone in different doses. Thus during infusion of 0.2 µg/kg/minute of PGE_1 in unanesthetized dogs, the FFA increased by 0.14 nmole/liter 20 minutes after the start of the infusion and gradually fell thereafter. With the dose 1.6 µg/kg, the FFA de- creased by 0.24 nmole/liter at the same time after the beginning of the infusion and remained low for a period of 30 minutes after the end of the infusion, strongly suggesting that the high con- centration of PGE_1 inhibits the FFA mobilization irrespective of any release of catecholamines. This is also in agreement with the observations of Steinberg and Vaughan (1967) that large doses of PGE_1 (50 µg/kg) in the dog lower the plasma FFA. On the other hand, PGA_1 (PGE_1-217, 20 µg/kg) increases the plasma FFA (cf. Steinberg and Pittman, 1966).

In low doses, 0.056–0.2 μg/kg/minute PGA$_1$ caused no consistent changes in the plasma levels of FFA, glycerol, or blood glucose in anesthetized dogs (Bergström *et al.*, 1967).

The nutritional state of the animal may also be of importance. Thus Berti *et al.* (1966) observed that although infusion of PGE$_1$ in a dose of 5.6 μg/kg/minute lowered plasma FFA in the rat, it had no effect in fasting animals.

Since the experiments *in vivo* with both dogs and human subjects were made in the fasting state, the inhibition may be less apparent. The infusion of 0.2 μg/kg/minute of PGE$_1$ in fed dogs increased the FFA levels (Bergström *et al.*, 1966b).

The action of prostaglandins on the mobilization fats and on the lipolytic effect of sympathomimetics *in vitro* and *in vivo* initially created a somewhat complex picture. However, it appears that the "genuine" effect of PGE$_1$ is to inhibit FFA mobilization and that this effect does not have to be dependent on catecholamine release. The lipolytic effect observed in some experiments with infusion of prostaglandins is most likely secondary to reflex catecholamine release, which has not been effectively inhibited by the PGE$_1$ doses used.

This conclusion is also indirectly supported by the observation that PGE$_1$ lacks effect on plasma FFA in patients with postural hypotension who are unable to respond to a fall in blood pressure with increased release of noradrenaline (Carlson, 1966).

Of the many effects that have been described for the prostaglandins, the antilipolytic effects seem to merit special consideration. The effects can be demonstrated even with very low concentrations or amounts of PGE$_1$, which seems to be the most active compound in this respect. The evidence for a physiological role is so far only circumstantial, but it seems hard to believe that it should be merely a side-effect without biological significance. The field is open for conjecture, particularly in view of the release of prostaglandins from the epididymal fat pad on nerve stimulation reported by Shaw (1966). It might also be postulated that prostaglandins, when accompanying the spermatozoa on their way to the ovum, effect the ovum itself or nidation, although a restriction of a local antilipolytic effect to the human and a few other species would appear strange.

The unusually high content of noradrenaline in the male accessory genital organs producing prostaglandins may also be brought out in connection with the peculiar interaction of the two types of hormones with respect to lipolysis on the same grounds that would obtain for the synergistic action on smooth muscle. A final judgment on the possible significance of these effects must be postponed, however, until more data have been produced.

3. Action on Glucose Uptake and Plasma Glucose

The glucose uptake in rat adipose tissue is stimulated by PGE_1 at concentrations of 0.1 or 0.4 μg/ml, although PGA_1 was without effect. If radioactive glucose is administered to rats, the uptake of radioactivity in fatty acids is increased by insulin and decreased by adrenaline. PGE_1 increases the labeling of fatty acids and also increases the synthesis of glycogen (Vaughan, 1967).

Böhle *et al.* (1966) studied the effect of PGE_1 on the carbohydrate and fat metabolism of isolated epididymal tissue in rats, using glucose-containing buffers with and without addition of insulin (0.5 milliunits/ml), adrenaline (0.1 μg/ml) and human growth hormone (25 μg/ml). PGE_1 was found to release glycerol to a greater extent than insulin and decreased the STH- and adrenaline-induced liberation of glycerol. The same authors also found that PGE_1 increased the oxidation of $1\text{-}^{14}C$-glucose to $^{14}CO_2$ by 70%, which is about one tenth of the effect of 0.5 milliunits of insulin. The effect of PGE_1 on glucose oxidation was increased by adrenaline and growth hormone. PGE_1 enhanced the increase in glucose uptake caused by adrenaline and increased by about 80% the incorporation of $1\text{-}^{14}C$-glucose into the lipids of the epididymal fat. The stimulating effect of PGE_1 on glucose utilization is believed to indicate that it has regulatory effects on cellular metabolism that are closely related to its antilipolytic activity.

Infusion of PGE_1 in the dog does not seem to alter the plasma glucose (Bergström *et al.*, 1966a). Nor is the hyperglycemia caused by DMPP modified by PGE_1, as observed by the same authors (Fig. 4.46).

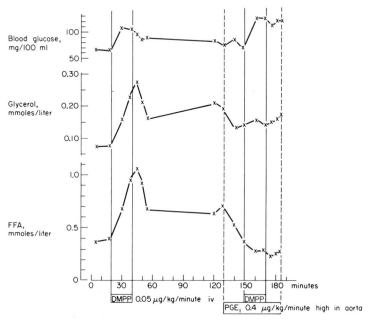

FIG. 4.46. Effect of PGE_1 on DMPP-induced changes in arterial plasma levels of FFA and glycerol and in blood glucose in one anesthetized, fasting dog. DMPP, a sympathetic ganglion-stimulating agent, was infused during two 20-minute periods. From 20 minutes before the second iv infusion, PGE_1 was administered high in aorta (after Bergström *et al.*, 1966b).

F. Antagonisms and Synergisms

Numerous attempts have been made to find specific prostaglandin antagonists, since this obviously would greatly assist in differentiating prostaglandins biologically from other substances with similar biological actions. Hitherto these efforts have been without much success, however. On the other hand, it has been observed (Eliasson, 1958b) that patulin, a bacteriostatic compound isolated from *Penicillium patulum* Bainier, abolished the action of PG substances on the isolated guinea pig ileum. In a dose of 6.4 μg/ml of bath fluid, patulin annulled the action of 0.04 and 0.2 units of PG and reduced the action of acetylcholine and 5-hydroxytryptamine, although it did not antagonize the action of BaCl$_2$ and even enhanced the effect of substance P.

In Section B of this chapter, a number of effects are described that may be relevant to the problems discussed in this section, among them alterations of sensitivity of a tachyphylactic character following addition of prostaglandins.

1. PROSTAGLANDINS AND SYMPATHOMIMETIC SUBSTANCES

a. *Blood Pressure and Circulation*

In earlier studies on the circulatory actions of purified extracts containing prostaglandins, it was noted that the effect of adrenaline was decreased after a previous dose of prostaglandin (von Euler, 1939). A similar antagonism was observed for PGE$_1$ and catecholamines (Steinberg *et al.*, 1963, 1964). The effect is not specific, since responses to angiotensin or vasopressin are similarly affected (Holmes *et al.*, 1963), and also occurs when bradykinin is used instead of PGE$_1$. It may be the result of a summation of a blood pressure raising and a lowering action (Carlson and Orö, 1966).

A sensitizing effect of PGE$_1$ on the myocardial cells of the guinea pig toward the effect of calcium has been reported by Mantegazza (1965).

b. *Guinea Pig Seminal Vesicle*

Goldblatt (1935) noted in his studies on the effect of extracts of human seminal fluid that adrenaline in small doses potentiated the effect of the extract on the isolated seminal vesicle of the guinea pig.

Clegg (1966a,b) studied the effect of PGE$_1$ and PGF$_{2\alpha}$ on the adrenaline-induced contraction of the guinea pig seminal vesicle and found a potentiation of this effect. On repeated administration the effect was reversed and inhibition ensued (Fig. 4.47). On the same preparation Eliasson and Risley (1966, 1967) observed that a small dose of PGE$_1$ without effect of its own

strongly potentiated the effect of adrenaline (Fig. 4.48). An effect
of this kind was in fact noticed by Chambers and Pickles (1958)
with menstrual lipids.

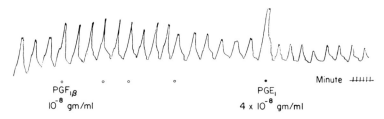

FIG. 4.47. Guinea pig seminal vesicle. The effect of $PGF_{1\beta}$ and PGE_1 on responses to adrenaline $(10^{-8}M)$ applied for 1 minute. At points indicated, prostaglandin was added with the adrenaline (after Clegg, 1966b).

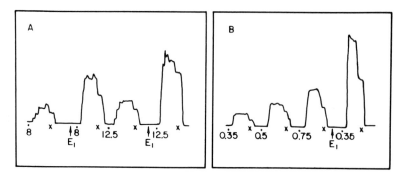

FIG. 4.48. Effect of prostaglandin E_1 ($E_1 = 0.5$ μg) on the response of the isolated seminal vesicle of guinea pig to adrenaline (A) and acetylcholine (B):
doses in μg; bath volume, 20 ml; x = wash twice (after Eliasson and Risley,
1966).

c. Uterus and Oviducts

Inhibitory effects of PGE_1 on the effect of adrenaline *in vivo*
have been observed on the rabbit oviduct. Thus after an injection
of 4 μg of PGE_1 intravenously, the increase in intraluminal
pressure produced by adrenaline is markedly reduced for some
10 minutes (Horton, 1966, p. 135). Similar effects of a crude
prostaglandin mixture were observed on the rabbit isolated oviduct (Horton *et al.*, 1965) (Fig. 4.49).

PGE₁ in a dose of 1–2 μg/kg was found to block the characteristic occlusion of the isthmus of the rabbit oviduct caused by
intravenous noradrenaline administration (Brundin, personal
communication).

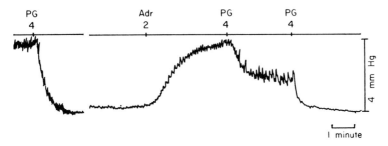

Fig. 4.49. Isolated rabbit oviduct suspended in a 4-ml bath containing aerated
Tyrode solution at 35°C. Record of intraluminal pressure. PG = crude prostaglandin mixture; Adr = adrenaline; doses in μg. Oviduct tone raised by adrenaline before the first dose of prostaglandin (after Horton *et al.*, 1965).

Pickles *et al.* (1966) and Clegg *et al.* (1966) have investigated
the potentiating effects of PGE and PGF upon the action of
several contracting substances on the guinea pig or rat myometrium. In addition to the transient but sometimes very marked
effect, the same authors have noted a prolonged enhancement
of the effects of spasmogens or electric field stimulation on the
guinea pig uterus.

In experiments on the isolated guinea pig uterus in diestrus
Clegg (1966b) has shown that PGF₂α in a concentration of 2
μg/ml completely prevents the inhibitory effect of 5 ng/ml of
noradrenaline on a subsequent dose of vasopressin (Fig. 4.50).

Uteri from guinea pigs in natural estrus respond to adrenaline
or noradrenaline with a contraction that is elicited by stimulation of α-receptors. This effect can be made to appear more regularly with the use of a β-receptor blocker such as propranolol
in 10 ng/ml doses. Upon exposure of the uterus to PGF₂α, two
types of inhibitory effects were observed by Clegg. In some cases
the response to noradrenaline was decreased, and in others noradrenaline caused maximal contraction only after washing out
the bath.

On the rat uterus, $PGF_{2\alpha}$ and PGE_1 caused a potentiation of the inhibitory effect of adrenaline or noradrenaline. After this potentiation, the responses to the amines diminished.

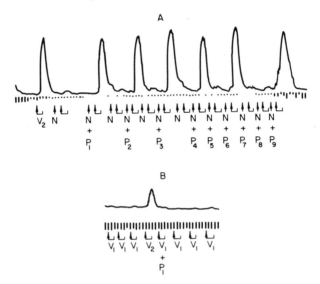

FIG. 4.50. The effect of $PGF_{2\alpha}$ on the responses of the diestrous guinea pig uterus to noradrenaline. A, regular submaximal responses to vasopressin were first obtained and at all points marked by ↑⎵ 2 mU of vasopressin was added to the 10-ml organ bath. A dose of noradrenaline was found that produced a marked inhibition of a subsequent response to vasopressin. At all points indicated by N, noradrenaline was applied for 1 minute, producing a bath concentration of 5×10^{-9} gm/ml. Then different amounts of $PGF_{2\alpha}$ were added with the noradrenaline (P_1–P_9) and the inhibitory effect of noradrenaline subsequently checked with vasopressin. ($P_1 = 3$ ng; $P_2 = 1$ ng; $P_3 = 0.1$ ng; P_4, $P_9 = 0.02$ ng; P_5, P_7, $P_8 = 0.01$ ng; $P_6 = 0.015$ ng). $PGF_{2\alpha}$ at a bath concentration of 2×10^{-12} gm/ml blocked the inhibitory effect of 5×10^{-9} gm/ml of noradrenaline. B shows the lack of effect of 3 ng of $PGF_{2\alpha}$ (P_1) on a threshold dose of vasopressin on the other uterine horn. Time marker shows 1-minute intervals. The concentrations of sympathomimetic in this and subsequent figures refer to the base (after Clegg, 1966b).

d. Vas Deferens

Holmes *et al.* (1963) observed that the contraction elicited by adrenaline from the vas deferens of the rabbit was counteracted by PGE_1 both *in vivo* and *in vitro*.

An interesting differentiation in the action of the prostaglandins on the stimulating effect of carbamylcholine and adrenaline was noted on the rat vas deferens. Thus PGE_1 antagonized the inhibitory effect of adrenaline seen for several other preparations, but it potentiated the action of carbamylcholine (Fig. 4.51).

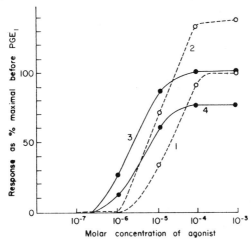

FIG. 4.51. The effect of PGE_1 on responses of rat vas deferens to carbamylcholine (interrupted line) and adrenaline (solid line). Curves 1 and 3 were made before exposure to prostaglandin; curves 2 and 4 were made 90 minutes after exposure to PGE_1; 4×10^{-6} gm/ml for 5 minutes (after Clegg, 1966b).

Adrenaline antagonism was insurmountable and could not be reversed by increasing the concentration of the agonist, and, as seen in the figure, it was still very marked 90 minutes after exposure of the preparation to 4×10^{-6} gm/ml of PGE_1 for 5 minutes. Similar effects were noted also for noradrenaline (in which the rat vas deferens is particularly rich) and phenylephrine. An initial potentiation of the response to sympathomimetics was noted in this preparation as on the rat uterus (Clegg, 1966b).

Mantegazza and Naimzada (1965) found no effect of PGE_1 in doses of 1–5 μg/ml on the stimulatory effect of sympathomimetic amines or of hypogastric stimulation on the vas deferens of the rat or the cat. On the other hand, PGE_1 increased these actions in the guinea pig and antagonized them in the rabbit.

PGE_1 was also able to restore the activity of sympathetic stimulation of the vas deferens in the guinea pig after it had been reduced by lowering the calcium concentration in the bath. The enhancing effect of PGE_1 on this preparation is interpreted to be a result of sensitization to the calcium effect.

e. Other Organs

A potentiation of the inhibitory effect of noradrenaline was also observed on tracheal preparations, for instance, on the rabbit tracheal chain. In a concentration of 1 ng/ml, PGE_1 potentiated the response to noradrenaline, whereas 60 ng/ml of PGE_1 alone had no action on the resting tone (Clegg, 1966b).

A prolonged, partial inhibitory effect of PGE_1, $PGF_{2\alpha}$, and $PGF_{1\beta}$ was observed also on the relaxing action of noradrenaline on the rat fundic strip as described by Vane (1957). The prostaglandins had a definite effect in bath concentrations as low as 10^{-11} to 10^{-10} gm/ml (Clegg, 1966b). Similar effects were noted with prostaglandins on the relaxing action of noradrenaline on rat colon.

The stimulating action of PGE_1 on the isolated stomach fundus strip is completely blocked by noradrenaline, although the acetylcholine response is not affected (Wolfe *et al.*, 1967).

The effects of different prostaglandins on the response to sympathomimetics on different organ preparations have been summarized by Clegg (1966b) (Table 4.XII).

From the findings reported, it is obvious that the prostaglandins inhibit the action of sympathomimetics, including noradrenaline itself, on a variety of organs, irrespective of whether the effect of the agonist is stimulation or inhibition. In some preparations the antagonism of an inhibitory effect is preceded by potentiation even if the action of prostaglandins themselves is one of stimulation. From her observations, Clegg concludes that prostaglandins do not occupy the adrenergic receptor (cf. Fig. 4.47), but may increase the affinity of sympathomimetics for adrenergic receptors by some kind of binding to it.

TABLE 4.XII

Preparations (Number of experiments)	Prostaglandin used (nature of direct effect)	Sympathomimetic and its effect	Effect of prostaglandin on response to sympathomimetic ($+$ = initial potentiation)
Rat vas deferens (31)	PGE_1 (0) $PGF_{2\alpha}$ (0)	Phenylephrine (+) Noradrenaline (+) Adrenaline (+) Isopropyl- (+) noradrenaline	Inhibition (+) Inhibition Inhibition (+) Inhibition
Rat colon (6)	PGE_1 (+) $PGF_{2\alpha}$ (+) $PGF_{1\beta}$	Noradrenaline (−) Adrenaline (−)	Inhibition Inhibition
Rat fundic strip (5)	PGE_1 (+) $PGF_{2\alpha}$ (+) $PGF_{1\beta}$	Noradrenaline (−)	(+) Inhibition
Guinea pig uterus (i) diestrus (stimulated by vasopressin) (3)	$PGF_{2\alpha}$ (+)	Noradrenaline (−)	Inhibition
(ii) estrous (in presence of a β-blocking agent) (3)	$PGF_{2\alpha}$ (+) PGE_1	Noradrenaline (+)	Inhibition
Rat uterus (electrically stimulated) (8)	$PGF_{2\alpha}$ (+) PGE_1 (+) $PGF_{1\beta}$	Noradrenaline (−) Adrenaline (−)	(+) Inhibition (+) Inhibition
Guinea pig tracheal preparations (contracted by carbamylcholine chloride 10^{-7} to 10^{-6} M (6)	PGE_1 (−) $PGF_{2\alpha}$	Noradrenaline (−) Isopropyl- (−) noradrenaline	Inhibition Inhibition
Rabbit tracheal chain (contracted by carbamylcholine chloride 10^{-7} to 10^{-6} M) (3)	PGE_1 (−) $PGF_{2\alpha}$ (−)	Adrenaline (−) Noradrenaline (−)	Potentiation
Guinea pig seminal vesicle (9)	PGE_1 $\left.\begin{array}{c} PGF_{1\beta} \\ PGF_{2\alpha} \end{array}\right\}$ (0)	Adrenaline (+)	(+) Inhibition

[a] After Clegg (1966b).

[b] In columns 2 and 3, 0 refers to no observed direct effect, + = stimulation, − = inhibition.

The physiological significance of the findings is not clear, particularly since prostaglandin is not present in significant concentrations in the reproductive organs of the animals on which the studies were made. It would therefore be of particular interest to repeat these experiments on human or sheep organs. If similar interactions obtain, which appears probable, these might play an important role, for instance, in the intricate reaction pattern serving the evacuation of the male accessory glands. As mentioned above, the vas deferens and the prostate gland are particularly rich in noradrenaline (von Euler, 1961; Sjöstrand, 1965). It does not appear inconceivable that the gradual accumulation of prostaglandin in the secretion of the seminal vesicle may induce initial effects of potentiation and secondary effects of inhibition on the adrenergically innervated smooth muscle that could be of importance in determining their contraction pattern in connection with sexual activity, as suggested earlier (von Euler, 1936). This type of prostaglandin effect may, of course, also operate on the smooth muscle of the female genital tract.

2. LIPOLYSIS

The discovery of the antagonistic action of prostaglandins on the lipolytic effect of sympathomimetics on adipose tissue by Steinberg et al. (1963), further studied by Steinberg et al. (1964), Bergström et al. (1964c, 1965a,b), Bergström and Carlson (1965b), Berti et al. (1966), and others, represents another example of an antagonism between prostaglandins and sympathomimetics. These effects are described in the previous section.

The antagonistic effect of PGE_1 on fat mobilization from the fat pad in vitro is not limited to sympathomimetics, but also applies to adrenocorticotropic hormone, glucagon, and thyroid-stimulating hormone (Steinberg et al., 1964). An analysis of its action showed that PGE_1 interfered with the adrenaline-induced activation of a hormone-sensitive lipase in adipose tissue. Moreover, a small but significant interaction with the activation of phosphorylase by adrenaline could be demonstrated. Of the different PG's, PGE_1 was highly active, but the PGF compounds had significantly smaller effects or were without action. Within the E series, the activity decreased in the order of $E_1 > E_2 > E_3$ (Steinberg and Vaughan, 1967). With respect to the mechanism of action for the inhibitory action of PGE compounds on the catecholamine-induced mobilization of FFA, it is assumed that PGE counteracts the formation of 3′,5′-AMP, which is facilitated by noradrenaline and other catecholamines. The cyclic nucleotide catalyzes the transformation from inactive to active lipase according to the scheme shown in Fig. 4.52 (Steinberg and Vaughan, 1967). The strong increase in the formation of cyclic AMP caused by caffeine plus adrenaline is effectively blocked by PGE_1 in a dose of 1 μg/ml (Butcher *et al.*, 1967). On isolated fat cells, PGE_1 has no effect.

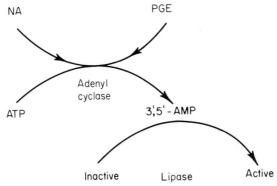

FIG. 4.52. Scheme for the transformation of inactive to active lipase (after Steinberg and Vaughan, 1967).

The increase in FFA release induced by theophylline *in vitro* on paired rat epididymal fat pads was antagonized by PGE_1, but the decreased triglyceride synthesis from glucose and palmitic acid also caused by theophylline was not influenced by PGE_1 (Sólyom *et al.*, 1967). It is concluded that both substances interfere with the breakdown of tissue triglycerides rather than with the resynthesis.

3. VARIOUS DRUG ACTIONS

As observed by Pickles *et al.* (1966), a small dose of PGE_1 (20 ng) caused a strong transient increase in the response of the guinea pig uterus to vasopressin *in vitro* (Fig. 4.53). The authors distinguish between the first response, which is called short-term potentiation, and the following increased responses, which are called enhancement. In addition to vasopressin, the potentiation has been observed with acetylcholine, histamine, and oxytocin.

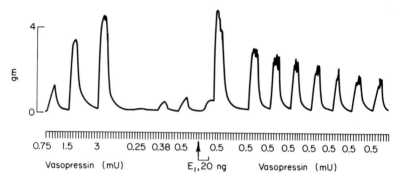

FIG. 4.53. Short-term "potentiation" and long-term "enhancement" by PGE₁ of vasopressin responses of guinea pig uterus *in vitro*. The first vasopressin response after the PGE₁ is "potentiated"; the subsequent ones "enhanced." The suspension medium contained 0.3 mM [Ca^{2+}], and 10 mM [Mg^{2+}]. Time marker, 1 minute (after Pickles *et al.*, 1966).

The pressor response to vasopressin and angiotensin in the rabbit was decreased similarly to that for adrenaline (Holmes *et al.*, 1963).

In their study on the isolated guinea pig seminal vesicle Eliasson and Risley (1966, 1967) also observed that PGE₁ strongly potentiated the effect of acetylcholine in a way similar to that with adrenaline or noradrenaline.

On the rat vas deferens, PGE₁ was found to potentiate the effect of carbamylcholine, although it antagonized the inhibitory effect of adrenaline (Clegg, 1966b).

Orloff *et al.* (1965) have shown that PGE₁ inhibits the response on the permeability of the toad bladder to antidiuretic hormone and theophylline. The site of action of the prostaglandins in this effect is not known.

The response to electric stimulation is also increased by addition of PGF or PGE to the guinea pig uterus bath. This effect is accompanied by depolarization measured with the sucrose-gap method, but not by consistent changes in the resting membrane potential. It still occurs in the presence of a β-blocking agent or after treatment with butacaine (Pickles *et al.*, 1966). It therefore appears to be different from the catecholamine effects described above.

G. Special Effects

1. PERMEABILITY RESPONSE OF TOAD BLADDER

The osmotic flow of water across the isolated bladder of *Bufo marinus* can be increased by adding vasopressin, theophylline, or adenosine 3′,5′-monophosphate (cyclic AMP) on the serosal side. It has been suggested that vasopressin exerts its effect by increasing the tissue concentration of cyclic AMP and that theophylline acts in a similar manner by decreasing the breakdown of this compound to inactive 5′-adenosine monophosphate, presumably by inhibiting phosphodiesterase (Orloff and Handler, 1962; Butcher and Sutherland, 1962).

Addition of PGE_1 (1.7×10^{-6} to 1.7×10^{-10} gm/ml) to the bath fluid on the serosal side reversibly diminishes the permeability response to vasopressin and theophylline, but not to cyclic AMP. Application of PGE_1 on the mucosal side was ineffective (Orloff *et al.*, 1965). PGE_1 alone had no effect. Control experiments with ricinoleic acid did not reveal any activity of this fatty acid on the vasopressin-, theophylline-, or cyclic AMP-induced increase in permeability.

The effect of PGE_1 suggests that it interferes with the formation of cyclic AMP and not with the action of this compound (see also Section E,1).

2. MICROBIAL GROWTH

Some fatty acids have antimicrobial activity and, therefore, an attempt was made to discover whether prostaglandin might also have such an effect. At a concentration of 1 mg/ml, PGE_1 was, however, inactive against all tested microorganisms, i.e., *Staphylococcus aureus, Streptococcus faecalis, Escherichia coli, Aspergillus niger, Trichophyton mentagrophytes,* and *Candida albicans.* Of a number of other acids tested, only ricinoleic and ricinelaidic acid showed any appreciable activity (Holmes, 1965).

3. PLATELET AGGREGABILITY

Normal platelets become adhesive and aggregate when exposed to collagen or adenosine diphosphate (ADP), a reactivity pattern that plays an important role in the early phase of thrombus formation.

Kloeze (1967) made the very interesting observation that PGE_1 in doses of 0.01–5 μg/ml of plasma markedly inhibited the ADP-induced aggregation of platelets from man, pig, and rat studied turbidometrically according to Born (1962) (Fig. 4.54). In contrast to this, PGE_2 enhanced the response to ADP when tested on rat and pig platelets. Tested on human platelets, PGE_2 had some inhibitory action at high concentration (Fig. 4.54), but

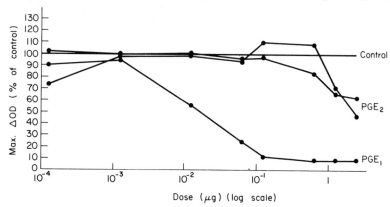

FIG. 4.54. Effect of PGE_1 and PGE_2 on ADP-induced (0.15 μg/ml) aggregation of human platelets in citrated plasma studied turbidometrically (after Kloeze, 1967).

it could not be excluded that this owed to contamination with PGE_1. Other prostaglandins inhibiting the ADP-induced aggregation of rat platelets were PGA_1, iso-PGE_1, and dinor-PGE_1. A number of the investigated prostaglandins were without effect in doses up to 1 μg/ml, e.g., $PGF_{1\alpha}$, PGB_1, PGB_2, and nor-PGE_1.

The adhesiveness of the rat platelets, studied according to Hellem *et al.* (1963), was not changed by the addition of PGE_1 (1 μg/ml) to citrated platelet-rich plasma. On the other hand, PGE_1 markedly inhibited the ADP-induced adhesiveness, although PGE_2 also in this test system had the opposite effect (Kloeze, 1967).

Recently, Emmons *et al.* (1967) demonstrated that PGE_1 also inhibits the adhesiveness and aggregation of human platelets induced by noradrenaline, ADP, ATP, 5-hydroxytryptamine, and connective tissue extract. It also inhibits the changes in platelet electrophoretic mobility produced by ADP and noradrenaline. The addition of Ca^{2+} ions counteracts the inhibitory effects of PGE_1. Intravenous infusion of 0.1–0.2 μg of PGE_1/kg/minute for 10 minutes into volunteers markedly reduced the aggregability of the platelets during a few hours (Hampton and Mitchell, personal communication).

The inhibitory action of PGE_1 on the ADP-induced adhesiveness and aggregation of human platelets has been confirmed by Eliasson (unpublished). The same effect was also noted for dog platelets. $PGF_{1\alpha}$ and $PGF_{2\alpha}$ were without effect (Bygdeman and Eliasson, unpublished).

4. Effect on Mast Cells

The observation that some prostaglandin actions seem to be related to the transport of calcium ions prompted Cabut and Vincenzi (1967) to study the effect of PGE_1 on mast cell degranulation and histamine and heparin release in the presence of various calcium concentrations.

In the presence of Ca^{2+}, prostaglandin E_1–like compound 48/80–caused a degranulation and disruption of incubated rat mesenteric mast cells. The optimal effect was obtained when the incubation contained 0.9 mM Ca^{2+} and 0.5 μg of PGE_1/ml. Higher and lower calcium concentrations decreased the number of disrupted cells. In contrast to PGE_1, the effect of compound

48/80 was higher with 1.8 mM calcium than with 0.9 mM (Fig. 4.55).

Release of biosynthesized, labeled histamine and heparin from suspended rat mesenteric cells was likewise dependent on calcium concentration and the amount of PGE_1. A liberation was evident at a concentration of 0.2 μg of PGE_1/ml, reached a maximum at 0.5 μg/ml, and was hardly significant at 2–5 μg/ml if the calcium concentration was 0.9 mM. The hypothesis was forwarded that prostaglandin-like compounds may be of importance to the release of biologically active compounds from mast cells (Cabut and Vincenzi, 1967).

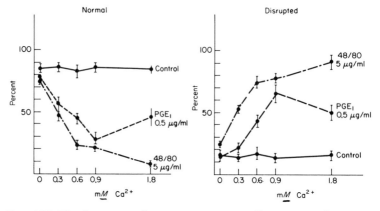

FIG. 4.55. The disruption of rat mesenteric mast cells *in vitro* in the presence of PGE_1 or compound 48/80 is dependent on the calcium concentration in the incubation medium (after Cabut and Vincenzi, 1967).

5. INFLUENCE ON SPERMATOZOA

There is no evidence for an effect of the prostaglandins on the motility or the maintenance of the spontaneous activity of the sperm cells (cf. Eliasson, 1959).

Addition of a prostaglandin extract did not change the oxygen consumption of washed human spermatozoa suspended in Krebs-Ringer phosphate buffer (Eliasson, 1959). Nor did PGE_1 change the metabolism of the ^{14}C-labeled fructose or the oxygen consumption by twice-washed human spermatozoa (White, Murdoch, and Eliasson, to be published).

In order to study whether the prostaglandins interacted with the aggregation of the spermatozoa, ADP was added to human semen or to carefully washed human spermatozoa suspended in citrated blood plasma. In none of the experiments, however, did ADP (up to 8 μg/ml) cause a visible aggregation of the sperm cells (Eliasson and Treichl, unpublished).

Aggregation of spermatozoa to each other or to other cell elements in the semen is not unusual and the possibility that this phenomenon in certain cases may be related to the prostaglandin content in semen should be further investigated.

5/Relations of Prostaglandins to Other Lipid Acids Active on Smooth Muscle

A. Vesiglandin

In connection with the findings of vasodepressor activity in extracts of the vesicular glands of man and certain animals (von Euler, 1934), it was observed that extracts of the vesicular gland as well as of semen of the monkey *(Macacus rhesus)* produced a sharp drop in the blood pressure of the atropinized rabbit. The depressor principle was readily inactivated by treatment with acid and alkali (von Euler, 1935b, 1936). Although extracts of human seminal fluid and sheep vesicular gland had similar activity on the blood pressure and, in addition, had strong smooth muscle-stimulating properties, e.g., on the intestine, the extract of vesicular gland from monkey had only slight effects of this kind (von Euler, 1936). It was therefore obvious that the latter principle differed from that in the sheep's vesicular gland. The compound was named vesiglandin (von Euler, 1935b). Its solubility and stability properties are similar to those found for the PG compounds.

Daniels *et al.* (1965) have drawn attention to the fact that PGA_1 (PGE_1-217) has a marked depressor action comparable to that of PGE_1, but only about a hundredth the smooth muscle-stimulating activity of PGE_1. The possibility should therefore be considered that vesiglandin may be closely related to PGA_1.

B. Irin

A smooth muscle-stimulating agent called irin, acidic in nature, obtained from rabbit iris, was described by Ambache (1957a). It could be shown that it was an unsaturated compound (Ambache, 1957b) and a hydroxy fatty acid (Ambache and Reynolds, 1959). Further studies showed that the biologically active ricinoleic acid, like irin, was inactivated by phenyl isocyanate, though oleic acid, which lacks a hydroxyl group on C-12, is inactive. The results indicate that the effect is dependent on the presence of an OH group (Ambache, 1959). Since the properties of irin suggested that it might be related to the prostaglandins, this possibility was studied by Änggård and Samuelsson (1964b), who succeeded in isolating $PGF_{2\alpha}$ from sheep iris.

When using a preparation allowing perfusion of the anterior chamber of the rabbit's eye under maintained pressure, Ambache et al. (1965) were able to show that an irin-like substance was released as a result of various forms of mechanical stimuli (cf. Ramwell, 1966).

C. Menstrual Fluid Factors

Pickles (1957, 1959) and Chambers and Pickles (1958) reported that acetone extracts of human menstrual fluid and endometrium contained smooth muscle-stimulating lipids. By use of column chromatography, the activity in the crude extract was separated into three components named A, B, and C (Clitheroe and Pickles, 1961). The more polar component A contained the major part of the biological activity. Further purification of this factor showed that it consisted of $PGF_{2\alpha}$ (first referred to as A-1) and also some PGE_2 (component A-2) (Eglinton et al., 1963). Component B seems to be a mixture of hydroxy and unsaturated long-chain fatty acids with smooth muscle-stimulating properties (guinea pig). It has been suggested that some of these acids may be precursors of the endometrial prostaglandins (Hall, 1966). Component C is the least polar and is apparently not acidic in nature. Further data on its chemical properties are, however, not available.

D. Darmstoff

Vogt (1949) detected a smooth muscle-stimulating principle in dialyzates from frog intestine and later in extracts of horse intestine. In such extracts, a phosphatidic acid with smooth-muscle-stimulating properties was found (Vogt, 1957). In later experiments, prostaglandins E_1 and F_1 could be tentatively identified in extract of dialyzates of frog intestine (Suzuki and Vogt, 1965). A comparison between frog darmstoff and that prepared from horse intestine revealed that the latter extract contains acidic phosphatides as major active constituents in contrast to the former (Vogt *et al.*, 1966). These authors have suggested that unsaturated fatty acids may be released from phosphatides by phospholipase A and later converted to prostaglandins that are diffusible. The smooth-muscle-contracting phosphatides, on the other hand, are bound to cellular structures and are extractable only after disintegration of the tissue (cf. Vogt *et al.*, 1967).

E. Other Factors

Incubation of egg yolk with cobra venom or lecithin from egg yolk with phospholipase A liberates a factor acting as a spasmogen on isolated guinea pig ileum (Feldberg *et al.*, 1938; Vogt, 1956). The active principle is usually called SRS-C (slow-reacting substance C). Dakhil and Vogt (1962) found that triphenylphosphine treatment inactived SRS-C, but did not affect the smooth-muscle-stimulating properties of partially purified prostaglandin. On the other hand, SRS-C obtained from perfusates of guinea pig lungs that had been injected with the venom or phospholipase A was only slightly reduced by the same treatment. During thin-layer chromatography, the active factors run like prostaglandin, indicating that they consist mainly of prostaglandin-like hydroxy acids (Babilli and Vogt, 1964).

The prostaglandin-like compounds are not preformed in the guinea pig lungs, but are released by the venoms. According to Vogt *et al.* (1967) they are most likely formed from free fatty acid precursors released from tissue phosphatides by venom phospholipase A. It is also thought that such compounds are formed in the frog intestine by endogenous phospholipases.

Another so-called slow-reacting substance (SRS-A) is obtained from sensitized lung tissue in contact with the antigen (A for anaphylaxis) (Brocklehurst, 1953, 1956, 1963). By chromatographing on silicic acid, Anderson *et al.* (1963) could separate the total smooth-muscle-stimulating activity into seven fractions. Chemical analyses indicated that SRS-A was a mixture of glycosides of neuraminic acid. Uvnäs (1965) could not identify SRS-A with prostaglandins.

Human serum contains a smooth-muscle-stimulating factor known as "G-acid." The structure $\Delta^{3,4}$-octadecenoic acid has been proposed (Gabr, 1956, 1961). Since there is no report that any nonhydroxylated fatty acid is spasmogenic (Ambache, 1963, 1966; Dakhil and Vogt, 1962), the chemical identity of G-acid may require reinvestigation.

From rabbit renal medulla, Lee *et al.* (1965) isolated three smooth-muscle-stimulating lipids preliminarily named "medullin," "compound 1," and "compound 2." All three factors possess smooth muscle-stimulating properties when tested on isolated pieces of the gastrointestinal tract, but only medullin and compound 2 are also hypotensive in action. From chemical analyses, it now appears that medullin has been identified as PGA_1. Compound 2 has tentatively been identified as PGE_2 (Muirhead *et al.*, 1967; Lee, 1967). Compound 1 is so far unidentified, but has biological properties in common with the PGF compounds. The occurrence of prostaglandins and other vasodepressor lipids in renal medulla was also described by Hickler and Strong and their associates (for ref., see Hickler *et al.*, 1964a,b; Strong *et al.*, 1966).

Crundwell *et al.* (1965) have described the synthesis of fatty acids with smooth-muscle-stimulant activity. The 12-hydroxy-heptadec-*trans*-10-enoic acid synthesized represents a fragment of a prostaglandin.

Extracts of human placenta contain smooth-muscle-stimulating fatty acids (Ichikawa, 1960). It appears that the activity is associated with the blood vessels, since Karim (1967) could isolate four different prostaglandins (E_1, E_2, $F_{1\alpha}$, and $F_{2\alpha}$) from the placental and umbilical vessels but not from the placental tissue. Oxytocic lipids are also present in human amniotic fluid (Hawkins, 1962; Landesman and Wilson, 1966).

From studies on the biological activity of fatty acids of various composition by Ambache (1966), it became clear that not only the hydroxy group is essential for the action, but also the acid group. In accordance with this, Pickles and Ward (1965) found a fatty alcohol in menstrual fluid that was nearly devoid of action on the guinea pig uterus, which was also the case with a rabbit ileum cerebroside in Vogt's (1960) experiments. When the neutral phospholipid lysolecithin was converted to lysophosphatidic acid, its activity increased some 500 times (Vogt, 1958).

Dakhil and Vogt (1962) have shown that arachidonic, linolenic, and linoleic acids do not contract the isolated guinea pig ileum, but that they become potent spasmogens after treatment with H_2O_2 or after contact with the air for some days. The spasmogenic activity could be destroyed by reducing agents, indicating that formation of hydroperoxides was the cause of the smooth-muscle-stimulating property.

For an extensive discussion of the relationships between chemical constitution and biological activity of fatty acids see Vogt (1958), Ambache (1959, 1963, 1966), and Ambache et al. (1963).

BIBLIOGRAPHY

Reviews

Bergström, S. (1965). The Prostaglandins and Their Influence on Lipid Metabolism. *J. Am. Oil Chemists Soc.* **42**, 608–609.

Bergström, S., and Samuelsson, B. (1965). Prostaglandins. *Ann. Rev. Biochem.* **34**, 101–108.

Bergström, S. (1967). Prostaglandins: Members of a New Hormonal System. *Science* **157**, 382–391.

Eliasson, R. (1959). Studies on Prostaglandin—Occurrence, Formation, and Biological Action. *Acta Physiol. Scand.* **46**, Suppl. 158, 1–73.

Horton, E. W. (1965). Biological Activities of Pure Prostaglandins. *Experientia* **21**, 113–118.

"Nobel Symposium II, Prostaglandins, Stockholm, 1966" (1967). Almqvist & Wiksell, Stockholm.

Pickles, V. R., and Fitzpatrick, R. J. (eds.) (1966). "Memoirs of the Society for Endocrinology." Cambridge Univ. Press, London and New York.

Pickles, V. R. (1967). The Prostaglandins. *Biol. Rev. Cambridge Phil. Soc.*, in press.

Samuelsson, B. (1965). Die Prostaglandine. *Angew. Chem.* **10**, 445–452.

References

Abrahamsson, S. (1963). *Acta Cryst.* **16**, 409–418.

Abrahamsson, S., Bergström, S., and Samuelsson, B. (1962). *Proc. Chem. Soc.* p. 332.

Adamson, U., Eliasson, R., and Wiklund, B. (1967). *Acta Physiol. Scand.* (in press).

Änggård, E. (1964). *Proc. 6th Intern. Congr. Biochem., New York, 1964* Abstr. No. VII, p. 562.

Änggård, E. (1965). *Biochem. Pharmacol.* **14**, 1507–1516.

Änggård, E. (1966a). Prostaglandins in the lung. M.D. Thesis, Karolinska Inst., Stockholm.

Änggård, E. (1966b). *Acta Physiol. Scand.* **66**, 509–510.

Änggård, E., and Bergström, S. (1963). *Acta Physiol. Scand.* **58**, 1–12.

Änggård, E., and Samuelsson, B. (1963). *Acta Physiol. Scand.* **59**, Suppl. 213, 170.

Änggård, E., and Samuelsson, B. (1964a). *J. Biol. Chem.* **239**, 4097–4102.

Änggård, E., and Samuelsson, B. (1964b). *Biochem. Pharmacol.* **13**, 281–283.

Änggård, E., and Samuelsson, B. (1965a). *J. Biol. Chem.* **240**, 3518–3521.

Änggård, E., and Samuelsson, B. (1965b). *Biochemistry* **4**, 1864–1871.

Änggård, E., and Samuelsson, B. (1966). *Arkiv Kemi* **25**, 293–300.

Änggård, E., Gréen, K., and Samuelsson, B. (1965). *J. Biol. Chem.* **240**, 1932–1940.

Ambache, N. (1957a). *J. Physiol. (London)* **135**, 114–132.

Ambache, N. (1957b). *J. Physiol. (London)* **138**, 6P–7P.

Ambache, N. (1959). *J. Physiol. (London)* **146**, 255–294.

Ambache, N. (1963). *In* "Comparative Endocrinology" (U.S. von Euler and H. Heller, eds.), Vol. II, pp. 128–158. Academic Press, New York.

Ambache, N. (1966) *In* "Memoirs of the Society for Endocrinology" (V. R. Pickles and R. J. Fitzpatrick, eds.), No. 14, pp. 19–28. Cambridge Univ. Press, London and New York.

Ambache, N., and Reynolds, M. (1959). *J. Physiol. (London)* **147**, 28P–29P.

Ambache, N., and Reynolds, M. (1960). *J. Physiol. (London)* **154**, 40P.

Ambache, N., Reynolds, M., and Whiting, J. M. C. (1963). *J. Physiol. (London)* **166**, 251–283.

Ambache, N., Kavanagh, L., and Whiting, J. (1965). *J. Physiol. (London)* **176**, 378–408.

Ambache, N., Kavanagh, L., and Whiting, J. (1966a). *J. Physiol. (London)* **182**, 110–130.

Ambache, N., Brummer, H. C., Rose, J. G., and Whiting, J. (1966b). *J. Physiol. (London)* **185**, 77P–78P.

Amersbach, R. (1930). *Muench. Med. Wochschr.* **77**, 225–227.

Anderson, D. M., Goadby, P., and Smith, W. G. (1963). *Biochem. Pharmacol.* **12**, 1037–1045.

Asplund, J. (1947a). *Acta Physiol. Scand.* **13**, 103–108.

Asplund, J. (1947b). *Acta Physiol. Scand.* **13**, 109–114.

Asplund, J. (1952). *Acta Radiol. Suppl.* **91**, 63–71.

Avanzino, G. L., Bradley, P. B., and Wolstencroft, J. H. (1966). *Brit. J. Pharmacol.* **27**, 157–162.

Avanzino, G. L., Bradley, P. B., and Wolstencroft, J. H. (1967). *Nobel Symp. II Prostaglandins, Stockholm, 1966* pp. 261–264. Almqvist & Wiksell, Stockholm.

Babilli, S., and Vogt, W. (1964). *J. Physiol. (London)* **177**, 31P–32P.

Bagli, J. F., Bogri, T., and Deghenghi, R. (1966). *Tetrahedon Letters* **5**, 465–470.

Barret, C. B., Dallas, M. S. J., and Padley, F. B. (1962). *Chem. Ind. (London)* p. 1050.

Battez, G., and Boulet, L. (1913). *Compt. Rend. Soc. Biol.* **74**, 8–9.

Beal, P. F., Babcock, J., and Lincoln, F. H. (1966). *J. Am. Chem. Soc.* **88**, 3131–3133.

Beal, P. F., Babcock, J., and Lincoln, F. H. (1967). *Nobel Symp. II, Prostaglandins, Stockholm, 1966* pp. 219–230. Almqvist & Wiksell, Stockholm.

Belonoschkin, B. (1949). "Zeugung beim Menschen." Sjöbergs Förlag, Stockholm.

Bergström, S. (1949). *Nord. Med.* **42**, 1465–1466.

Bergström, S., and Carlson, L. A. (1965a). *Acta Physiol. Scand.* **64**, 479–480.

Bergström, S., and Carlson, L. A. (1965b). *Acta Physiol. Scand.* **63**, 195–196.

Bergström, S., and Samuelsson, B. (1962). *J. Biol. Chem.* **237**, 3005–3006.

Bergström, S., and Samuelsson, B. (1963). *Acta Chem. Scand.* **17**, 282–287.

Bergström, S., and Sjövall, J. (1957). *Acta Chem. Scand.* **11**, 1086.

Bergström, S., and Sjövall, J. (1960a). *Acta Chem. Scand.* **14**, 1693–1700.

Bergström, S., and Sjövall, J. (1960b). *Acta Chem. Scand.* **14**, 1701–1705.

Bergström, S., and von Euler, U. S. (1963). *Acta Physiol. Scand.* **59**, 493–494.

Bergström, S., Dunér, H., von Euler, U. S., Pernow, B., and Sjövall, J. (1959a). *Acta Physiol. Scand.* **45**, 145–151.

Bergström, S., Eliasson, R., von Euler, U. S., and Sjövall, J. (1959b). *Acta Physiol. Scand.* **45**, 133–144.

Bergström, S., Krabisch, L., and Sjövall, J. (1960). *Acta Chem. Scand.* **14**, 1706–1710.

Bergström, S., Krabisch, L., Samuelsson, B., and Sjövall, J. (1962a). *Acta Chem. Scand.* **16**, 969–974.

Bergström, S., Ryhage, R., Samuelsson, B., and Sjövall, J. (1962b). *Acta Chem. Scand.* **16**, 501–502.

Bergström, S., Dressler, F., Ryhage, R., Samuelsson, B., and Sjövall, J. (1962c). *Arkiv Kemi* **19**, 563–567.

Bergström, S., Dressler, F., Krabisch, L., Ryhage, R., and Sjövall, J. (1962d). *Arkiv Kemi* **20**, 63–66.

Bergström, S., Ryhage, R., Samuelsson, B., and Sjövall, J. (1963a). *J. Biol. Chem.* **238**, 3555–3564.

Bergström, S., Ryhage, R., Samuelsson, B., and Sjövall, J. (1963b). *Acta Chem. Scand.* **17**, 2271–2280.

Bergström, S., Danielsson, H., and Samuelsson, B. (1964a). *Biochim. Biophys. Acta* **90**, 207–210.

Bergström, S., Danielsson, H., Klenberg, D., and Samuelsson, B. (1964b). *J. Biol. Chem.* **239**, PC4006–PC4008.

Bergström, S., Carlson, L. A., and Orö, L. (1964c). *Acta Physiol. Scand.* **60**, 170–180.

Bergström, S., Carlson, L. A., Ekelund, L. G., and Orö, L. (1965a). *Acta Physiol. Scand.* **64**, 332–339.

Bergström, S., Carlson, L. A., Ekelund, L. G., and Orö, L. (1965b). *Proc. Soc. Exptl. Biol. Med.* **188**, 110–112.

Bergström, S., Carlson, L. A., and Orö, L. (1966a). *Acta Physiol. Scand.* **67**, 185–193.

Bergström, S., Carlson, L. A., and Orö, L. (1966b). *Acta Physiol. Scand.* **67**, 141–151.

Bergström, S., Carlson, L. A., and Orö, L. (1967). *Life Sci.* **6**, 449–455.

Berry, P. A., and Collier, H. O. J. (1964). *Brit. J. Pharmacol.* **23**, 201–216.

Berti, F., Lentati, R., and Usardi, M. M. (1965). *Med. Pharmacol. Exptl.* **13**, 233–240.

Berti, F., Lentati, R., Usardi, M. M., and Paoletti, R. (1966). *Symp. Biophys. Physiol. Biol. Transport, Rome, 1965.*

Bickers, W. (1951). *Fertility Sterility* **2**, 342–346.

Böhle, E., Döbert, E., Ammon, J., and Ditschuneit, H. (1966). *Diabetologia* **2**, 162–168.

Bogri, T., Bagli, J. F., and Deghenghi, R. (1967). *Nobel Symp. II, Prostaglandins, Stockholm, 1966* pp. 231–236. Almqvist & Wiksell, Stockholm.

Born, G. V. R. (1962). *J. Physiol. (London)* **162**, 67P–68P.

Brocklehurst, W. E. (1953). *J. Physiol. (London)* **120**, 16P–17P.

Brocklehurst, W. E. (1956). *Ciba Found. Symp. Histamine* pp. 175–179.

Brocklehurst, W. E. (1963). *Biochem. Pharmacol.* **12**, 431–435.

Brundin, J. (1965). *Acta Physiol. Scand.* **66**, Suppl. 259.

Butcher, R. W., and Sutherland, E. W. (1962). *J. Biol. Chem.* **237**, 1244–1250.

Butcher, R. W., Pike, J. E., and Sutherland, E. W. (1967). *Nobel Symp. II, Prostaglandins, Stockholm, 1966* pp. 133–138. Almqvist & Wiksell, Stockholm.

Bygdeman, M. (1964). *Acta Physiol. Scand.* **63**, Suppl. 242.

Bygdeman, M. (1967). *Nobel Symp. II, Prostaglandins, Stockholm, 1966* pp. 63–70. Almqvist & Wiksell, Stockholm.

Bygdeman, M., and Eliasson, R. (1963a). *Acta Physiol. Scand.* **59**, 43–51.

Bygdeman, M., and Eliasson, R. (1963b). *Med. Exptl.* **9**, 409–415.

Bygdeman, M., and Eliasson, R. (1963c). *Experientia* **19**, 180–181.

Bygdeman, M., and Eliasson, R. (1963d). *Experientia* **19**, 650–653.

Bygdeman, M., and Eliasson, R. (1963e). *Med. Exptl.* **9**, 31–37.

Bygdeman, M., and Hamberg, M. (1967). *Acta Physiol. Scand.* **69**, 320–326.

Bygdeman, M., and Holmberg, O. (1966). *Acta Chem. Scand.* **20**, 2308–2310.

Bygdeman, M., and Samuelsson, B. (1964). *Clin. Chim. Acta* **10**, 566–568.

Bygdeman, M., and Samuelsson, B. (1966). *Clin. Chim. Acta* **13**, 465–474.

Bygdeman, M., Hamberg, M., and Samuelsson, B. (1966). *In* "Memoirs of the Society for Endocrinology" (V. R. Pickles and R. J. Fitzpatrick, eds.), No. 14, pp. 49–64. Cambridge Univ. Press, London and New York.

Bygdeman, M., Kwon, S., and Wiqvist, N. (1967). *Nobel Symp. II, Prostaglandins, Stockholm, 1966* pp. 93–96. Almqvist & Wiksell, Stockholm.

Cabut, M. S., and Vincenzi, L. (1967). *Nobel Symp. II, Prostaglandins, Stockholm, 1966.*

Caldeyro-Barcia, R. (1958). *Congr. Intern. Gynecol. Obstet., Montreal* Vol. I, p. 65. Montevideo, Uruguay.

Campbell, B., and Petersen, W. E. (1953). *Human Biol.* **25**, 165–168.

Carlson, L. A. (1965). *Ann. N. Y. Acad. Sci.* **131**, 119–142.

Carlson, L. A. (1966). *Progr. Biochem. Pharmacol.* **3** (in press).

Carlson, L. A. (1967). *Nobel Symp. II, Prostaglandins, Stockholm, 1966* pp. 122–132. Almqvist & Wiksell, Stockholm

Carlson, L. A., and Orö, L. (1966). *Acta Physiol. Scand.* **67**, 89–99.

Chambers, P. L., and Pickles, V. R. (1958). *J. Physiol. (London)* **144**, 68–79.

Clegg, P. C. (1966a). *Nature* **209**, 1137–1139.

Clegg, P. C. (1966b). *In* "Memoirs of the Society for Endocrinology" (V. R. Pickles and R. J. Fitzpatrick, eds.), No. 14, pp. 119–136. Cambridge Univ. Press, London and New York.

Clegg, P. C., Hall, W. J., and Pickles, V. R. (1966). *J. Physiol. (London)* **183**, 123–144.

Clitheroe, H. J. (1961). *J. Physiol. (London)* **155**, 62P–63P.

Clitheroe, H. J., and Pickles, V. R. (1961). *J. Physiol. (London)* **156**, 225–237.

Coceani, F., and Wolfe, L. S. (1965). *Can. J. Physiol. Pharmacol.* **43**, 445–450.

Coceani, F., and Wolfe, L. S. (1966). *Can. J. Physiol. Pharmacol.* **44**, 933–950.

Cockrill, J. R., Miller, E. G., Jr., and Kurzrok, R. (1935). *Am. J. Physiol.* **112**, 577–580.

Crowshaw, K. (1966). *Fed. Proc.* **25**, 765.

Crundwell, E., Pinnegar, M. A., and Templeton, W. (1965). *J. Med. Chem.* **8**, 41–45.

Csapo, A. (1954). *Am. J. Physiol.* **177**, 348–354.

Csapo, A. I., and Pinto-Dantas, C. R. (1966). *Fertil. Steril.* **17**, 34–38.

Dakhil, T., and Vogt, W. (1962). *Arch. Exptl. Pathol. Pharmakol.* **243**, 174–186.

Daniels, E. G., Hinman, J. W., Johnson, B. A., Kupiecki, F. P., Nelson, J. W., and Pike, J. E. (1965). *Biochem. Biophys. Res. Commun.* **21**, 413–417.

Davies, B. N., Horton, E. W., and Withrington, P. G. (1967). *J. Physiol. (London)* **188**, 38–39P.

DuCharme, D. W., and Weeks, J. R. (1967). *Nobel Symp. II, Prostaglandins, Stockholm, 1966* pp. 173–182. Almqvist & Wiksell, Stockholm.

Egli, G. E., and Newton, M. (1961). *Fertility Sterility* **12**, 151–155.

Eglinton, G., Raphael, R. A., Smith, G. N., Hall, W. J., and Pickles, V. R. (1963). *Nature* **200**, 960, 993–995.

Eliasson, R. (1958a). *Nature* **182**, 256–257.

Eliasson, R. (1958b). *Experientia* **14**, 460–461.

Eliasson, R. (1959). *Acta Physiol. Scand.* **46**, Suppl. 158.

Eliasson, R. (1961). *J. Urol.* **86**, 676–678.

Eliasson, R. (1963). Prostaglandin — Properties, Actions, and Significance. *Biochem. Pharmacol.* **12**, 405–412.

Eliasson, R. (1965). *J. Reprod. Fertility* **9**, 331–336.

Eliasson, R. (1966a). *In* "Memoirs of the Society for Endocrinology" (V. R. Pickles and R. J. Fitzpatrick, eds.), No. 14, pp. 77–88. Cambridge Univ. Press, London and New York.

Eliasson, R. (1966b). *Biochem. Pharmacol.* **15**, 755.

Eliasson, R. (1966c). *Acta Physiol. Scand.* **66**, 249–250.

Eliasson, R., and Posse, N. (1960). *Acta Obstet. Gynecol. Scand.* **39**, 112–126.

Eliasson, R., and Posse, N. (1965). *Intern. J. Fertility* **10**, 373–377.

Eliasson, R., and Risley, P. (1966). *Acta Physiol. Scand.* **67**, 253–254.

Eliasson, R., and Risley, P. L. (1967). *Nobel Symp. II, Prostaglandins, Stockholm, 1966* pp. 85–90. Almqvist & Wiksell, Stockholm.

Emmons, P. R., Hampton, J. R., Harrison, M. J. G., Honour, A. J., and Mitchell, J. R. A. (1967). *Brit. Med. J.* No. 5550, 468–472.

Feldberg, W., and Myers, R. D. (1966). *J. Physiol. (London)* **184**, 837–855.

Feldberg, W., and Sherwood, S. L. (1953). *J. Physiol. (London)* **120**, 3P–4P.

Feldberg, W., Holden, H. F., and Kellaway, C. H. (1938). *J. Physiol. (London)* **94**, 232–248.

Friberg, O. (1953). *Acta Endocrinol.* **12**, 193–196.

Gabr, Y. (1956). *Brit. J. Pharmacol.* **11**, 93–98.

Gabr, Y. (1961). *Brit. J. Pharmacol.* **17**, 51–58.

Goldblatt, M. W. (1933). *J. Soc. Chem. Ind. (London)* **52**, 1056–1057.

Goldblatt, M. W. (1935). *J. Physiol. (London)* **84**, 208–218.

Granström, E., Inger, U., and Samuelsson, B. (1965). *J. Biol. Chem.* **240**, 457–461.

Gréen, K., and Samuelsson, B. (1964). *J. Lipid Res.* **5**, 117–120.

Hall, W. J. (1966). *In* "Memoirs of the Society for Endocrinology" (V. R. Pickles and R. J. Fitzpatrick, eds.), No. 14, pp. 65–74. Cambridge Univ. Press, London and New York.

Hamberg, M., and Samuelsson, B. (1965a). *Biochim. Biophys. Acta* **106**, 215–217.

Hamberg, M., and Samuelsson, B. (1965b). *Biochem. Biophys. Res. Comm.* **21**, 531–536.

Hamberg, M., and Samuelsson, B. (1966). *J. Biol. Chem.* **241**, 257–263.

Hamberg, M., and Samuelsson, B. (1967). *Nobel Symp. II, Prostaglandins, Stockholm, 1966* pp. 63–70. Almqvist & Wiksell, Stockholm.

Hansson, E., and Samuelsson, B. (1965). *Biochem. Biophys. Acta* **106**, 379–385.

Harris, G. W., and Pickles, V. R. (1953). *Nature* **172**, 1049.

Hartman, C. G. (1957). *Fertility Sterility* **8**, 403–427.

Hauge, A., Lunde, P. K. M., and Waaler, B. A. (1967). *Life Sci.* **6**, 673–680.

Hawker, R. W., Roberts, V. S., and Walmsley, C. F. (1960). *Endocrinology* **67**, 187–193.

Hawkins, D. F. (1962). *Nature* **194**, 975–976.

Hawkins, D. F., and Labrum, A. H. (1956). *Brit. Med. J.* **II**, 1236.

Hawkins, D. F., and Labrum, A. H. (1961). *J. Reprod. Fertility* **2**, 1–10.

Hellem, A. J., Ödegaard, A. E., and Skålhegg, B. A. (1963). *Thromb. Diath. Haemorrhag.* **10**, 61.

Hickler, R. B., Lauler, D. P., and Saravis, C. A. (1964a). *Trans. Assoc. Am. Physicians* **77**, 196–200.

Hickler, R. B., Lauler, D. P., Saravis, C. A., Vagnucci, A. I., Steiner, G., and Thorn, G. W. (1964b). *Can. Med. Ass. J.* **90**, 280–287.

Holmes, S. W. (1965). *Nature* **206**, 405–406.

Holmes, S. W., and Horton, E. W. (1967). *J. Physiol. (London)* **191**, 134P–135P.

Holmes, S. W., Horton, E. W., and Main, I. H. M. (1963). *Brit. J. Pharmacol.* **21**, 538–543.

Horton, E. W. (1963). *Nature* **200**, 892–893.

Horton, E. W. (1964). *Brit. J. Pharmacol.* **22**, 189–192.

Horton, E. W. (1965). *Experientia* **21**, 113–118.

Horton, E. W. (1966). *In* "Memoirs of the Society for Endocrinology" (V. R. Pickles and R. J. Fitzpatrick, eds.), No. 14, p. 135. Cambridge Univ. Press, London and New York.

Horton, E. W., and Main, I. H. M. (1963). *Brit. J. Pharmacol.* **21**, 182–189.

Horton, E. W., and Main, I. H. M. (1965a). *J. Physiol. (London)* **179**, 18P–20P.

Horton, E. W., and Main, I. H. M. (1965b). *Brit. J. Pharmacol.* **24**, 470–476.

Horton, E. W., and Main, I. H. M. (1965c). *Intern. J. Neuropharmacol.* **4**, 65–69.

Horton, E. W., and Main, I. H. M. (1966a). *In* "Memoirs of the Society for Endocrinology" (V. R. Pickles and R. J. Fitzpatrick, eds.), No. 14, pp. 29–37. Cambridge Univ. Press, London and New York.

Horton, E. W., and Main, I. H. M. (1966b). *J. Physiol. (London)* **185**, 36–37P.

Horton, E. W., and Main, I. H. M. (1967). *Nobel Symp. II, Prostaglandins, Stockholm, 1966* pp. 253–260. Almqvist & Wiksell, Stockholm.

Horton, E. W., and Thompson, C. J. (1964). *Brit. J. Pharmacol.* **22**, 183–188.

Horton, E. W., Main, I. H. M., and Thompson, C. J. (1963). *J. Physiol. (London)* **168**, 54P–55P.

Horton, E. W., Main, I. H. M., and Thompson, C. J. (1965). *J. Physiol. (London)* **180**, 514–528.

Ichikawa, S. (1960). *Am. J. Physiol.* **198**, 1094–1098.

Joelsson, I., Ingelman-Sundberg, A., and Sandberg, F. (1966). *J. Obstet. Gynaecol. Brit. Commonwealth* **73**, 832–836.

Karim, S. M. M. (1967). *Brit. J. Pharmacol.* **29**, 230–237.

Karlson, S. (1944). *Acta Obstet. Gynecol. Scand.* **24**, Suppl. 4.

Karlson, S. (1949). *Nord. Med.* **42**, 1466.

Karlson, S. (1959). *Acta Obstet. Gynecol. Scand.* **38**, 503–521.

Kirschner, H., and Vogt, W. (1961). *Biochem. Pharmacol.* **8**, 224–234.

Kloeze, J. (1967). *Nobel Symp. II. Prostaglandins, Stockholm, 1966* pp. 241–252. Almqvist & Wiksell, Stockholm.

Krehbiel, R. H., and Carstens, H. P. (1938). *Anat. Record* **47**, Suppl. 70.

Krnjević, K. (1965). *Brit. Med. Bull.* **21**, 10–14.

Kupiecki, F. P. (1965). *Life Sci.* **4**, 1811–1815.

Kurzrok, R., and Lieb, C. C. (1930). *Proc. Soc. Exptl. Biol. Med.* **28**, 268–272.

Landesman, R., and Wilson, K. (1966). *Clin. Obstet. Gynecol.* **9**, 554–564.

Leaf, A., and Hayes, R. M. (1961). *Recent Progr. Hormone Res.* **17**, 467–492.

Lee, J. B. (1967). *Nobel Symp. II, Prostaglandins, Stockholm, 1966* pp. 197–210. Almqvist & Wiksell, Stockholm.

Lee, J. B., Covino, B. G., Takman, B. H., and Smith, E. R. (1965). *Circulation Res.* **17**, 57–77.

Linn, B. O., Shunk, C. H., Folkers, K., Ganley, O., and Robinson, H. J. (1961). *Biochem. Pharmacol.* **8**, 339–340.

Lundquist, F. (1949). *Acta Physiol. Scand.* **19**, Suppl. 66.

McCurdy, R., and Nakano, J. (1966). *Clin. Res.* **14**, 428.

Main, I. H. M. (1964). *Brit. J. Pharmacol.* **22**, 511–519.

Mann, T. (1964). "The Biochemistry of Semen and of the Male Reproductive Tract." Methuen, London.

Mann, T., Seamark, R. F., and Sharman, D. F. (1961). *Brit. J. Pharmacol.* **17**, 208–217.

Mantegazza, P. (1965). *Atti Accad. Med. Lombarda* **20**, 66–72.

Mantegazza, P., and Naimzada, M. K. (1965). *Atti Accad. Med. Lombarda* **20**, 58–64.

Masters, W. H., and Johnson, V. E. (1966). "Human Sexual Response." Little, Brown, Boston, Massachusetts.

Mattner, P. E. (1963a). *Australian J. Biol. Sci.* **16**, 688–694.

Mattner, P. E. (1963b). *Australian J. Biol. Sci.* **16**, 877–884.

Mattner, P. E., and Braden, A. W. H. (1963). *Australian J. Biol. Sci.* **16**, 473–481.

Miyazaki, E., Ishizawa, M., Sunano, S., Syuto, B., and Sakagami, T. (1967). *Nobel Symp. II, Prostaglandins, Stockholm, 1966* pp. 277–282. Almqvist & Wiksell, Stockholm.

Muirhead, E. E., Daniels, E. G., Pike, J. E., and Hinman, J. W. (1967). *Nobel Symp. II, Prostaglandins, Stockholm, 1966* pp. 183–196. Almqvist & Wiksell, Stockholm.

Nugteren, D. H., and van Dorp, D. A. (1965). *Biochim. Biophys. Acta* **98,** 654–656.

Nugteren, D. H., van Dorp, D. A., Bergström, S., Hamberg, M., and Samuelsson, B. (1966a). *Nature* **212,** 38–39.

Nugteren, D. H., Beerthuis, R. K., and van Dorp, D. A. (1966b). *Rec. Trav. Chim.* **85,** 405–419.

Orloff, J., and Handler, J. S. (1962). *J. Clin. Invest.* **41,** 702–709.

Orloff, J., Handler, J. S., and Bergström, S. (1965). *Nature* **205,** 397–398.

Paoletti, R., Lentati, R. L., and Korolkiewicz, Z. (1967). *Nobel Symp. II, Prostaglandins, Stockholm, 1966* pp. 147–160. Almqvist & Wiksell, Stockholm.

Parkes, G. H. (1931). *Phil. Trans. Roy. Soc. London* **B219,** 381–419.

Pickford, M. (1960). *In* "Polypeptides" (M. Schachter, ed.), pp. 42–48. Macmillan (Pergamon), New York.

Pickles, V. R. (1953). *J. Obstet. Gynaecol. Brit. Empire* **60,** 302–312.

Pickles, V. R. (1957). *Nature* **180,** 1198–1199.

Pickles, V. R. (1959). *J. Endocrinol.* **19,** 150–157.

Pickles, V. R. (1966). *J. Physiol. (London)* **183,** 69P–70P.

Pickles, V. R. (1967). *Nobel Symp. II, Prostaglandins, Stockholm, 1966* pp. 79–84. Almqvist & Wiksell, Stockholm.

Pickles, V. R., and Hall, W. J. (1963). *J. Reprod. Fertility* **6,** 315–317.

Pickles, V. R., and Ward, P. F. V. (1965). *J. Physiol. (London)* **178** 38P–39P.

Pickles, V. R., Hall, W. J., Best, F. A., and Smith, G. N. (1965). *J. Obstet. Gynaecol. Brit. Commonwealth* **72,** 185–192.

Pickles, V. R., Hall, W. J., Clegg, P. C., and Sullivan, T. J. (1966). *In* "Memoirs of the Society for Endocrinology" (V. R. Pickles and R. J. Fitzpatrick, eds.), No. 14, pp. 89–103. Cambridge Univ. Press, London and New York.

Pike, J. E., Kupiecki, F. P., and Weeks, J. R. (1967). *Nobel Symp. II, Prostaglandins, Stockholm, 1966* pp. 161–172. Almqvist & Wiksell, Stockholm.

Ramwell, P. W. (1965). *Proc. 23rd Intern. Congr. Physiol. Sci., Tokyo* Abstr. No. 953, p. 404.

Ramwell, P. W. (1966). *Federation Proc.* **25,** 627.

Ramwell, P. W., and Shaw, J. E. (1963a). *Life Sci.* **2,** 419–426.

Ramwell, P. W., and Shaw, J. E. (1963b). *J. Physiol. (London)* **169,** 51P–52P.

Ramwell, P. W., and Shaw, J. E. (1966). *Am. J. Physiol.* **211,** 125–134.

Ramwell, P. W., Shaw, J. E., and Kucharski, J. (1965). *Science* **149,** 1390–1391.

Ramwell, P. W., Shaw, J. E., Douglas, W. W., and Poisner, A. M. (1966a). *Nature* **210,** 273–274.

Ramwell, P. W., Shaw, J. E., and Jessup, R. (1966b). *Am. J. Physiol.* **211**, 998–1004.

Rowson, L. E. (1955). *Brit. Vet. J.* **3**, 334–342.

Rubin, I. C. (1947). "Uterotubal Insufflation," Mosby, St. Louis, Missouri.

Ryhage, R., and Samuelsson, B. (1965). *Biochem. Biophys. Res. Commun.* **19**, 279–282.

Samuelsson, B. (1963a). *Biochem. J.* **89**, 34P.

Samuelsson, B. (1963b). *J. Biol. Chem.* **238**, 3229–3234.

Samuelsson, B. (1963c). *J. Am. Chem. Soc.* **85**, 1878–1879.

Samuelsson, B. (1964a). *J. Biol. Chem.* **239**, 4091–4096.

Samuelsson, B. (1964b). *Biochim. Biophys. Acta* **84**, 218–219.

Samuelsson, B. (1964c). *Biochim. Biophys. Acta* **84**, 707–713.

Samuelsson, B. (1965a). *J. Am. Chem. Soc.* **87**, 3011–3013.

Samuelsson, B. (1965b). *Proc. 2nd Intern. Congr. Endocrinol., London, Excerpta Med. Found.* pp. 847–856.

Sandberg, F., Ingelman-Sundberg, A., and Rydén, G. (1963a). *J. Obstet. Gynaecol. Brit. Commonwealth* **70**, 130–134.

Sandberg, F., Ingelman-Sundberg, A., and Rydén, G. (1963b). *Acta Obstet. Gynecol. Scand.* **42**, 269–278.

Sandberg, F., Ingelman-Sundberg, A., and Rydén, G. (1964). *Acta Obstet. Gynaecol. Scand.* **43**, 95–102.

Sandberg, F., Ingelman-Sundberg, A., and Rydén, G. (1965). *Acta Obstet. Gynecol. Scand.* **44**, 585–594.

Sandberg, F., Ingelman-Sundberg, A., Joelsson, J., and Rydén, G. (1967). *Nobel Symp. II, Prostaglandins, Stockholm, 1966* pp. 91–92. Almqvist & Wiksell, Stockholm.

Sasamori, S. (1965). *Sapporo i gaku zasshi* **28**, 286–299.

Sawyer, W. H. (1961). *Pharmacol. Rev.* **13**, 225–277.

Schneider, W. P., Pike, J. E., and Kupiecki, F. P. (1966). *Biochim. Biophys. Acta* **125**, 611–613.

Schott, R. G., and Phillips, R. W. (1941). *Anat. Record* **79**, 531–540.

Shaw, J. E. (1965). *Proc. 23rd Intern. Congr. Physiol. Sci. Tokyo* p. 406.

Shaw, J. E. (1966). *Federation Proc.* **25**, 770.

Shaw, J. E., and Ramwell, P. W. (1967). *Nobel Symp. II, Prostaglandins, Stockholm, 1966* pp. 293–295. Almqvist & Wiksell, Stockholm.

Sjöstrand, N. (1965). *Acta Physiol. Scand.* **65**, Suppl. 257.

Sobrero, A. J., and MacLeod, J. (1962). *Fertility Sterility* **13**, 184–189.

Sólyom, A., Puglisi, L., and Muhlbachova, E. (1967). *Biochem. Pharmacol.* **16**, 521–525.

Starke, C. N. (1949). *Onderstepoort J. Vet. Res.* **22**, 415–425.

Steinberg, D., and Pittman, R. (1966). *Proc. Soc. Exp. Biol. Med.* **123**, 192–196.

Steinberg, D., and Vaughan, M. (1967). *Nobel Symp. II, Prostaglandins, Stockholm, 1966* pp. 109–122. Almqvist & Wiksell, Stockholm.

Steinberg, D., Vaughan, M., Nestel, P. J., and Bergström, S. (1963). *Biochem. Pharmacol.* **12**, 764–766.

Steinberg, D., Vaughan, M., Nestel, P. J., Strand, O., and Bergström, S. (1964). *J. Clin. Invest.* **43**, 1533–1540.

Stock, K., and Westermann, E. (1966). *Arch. Exptl. Pathol. Pharmakol.* **253**, 86–87.

Strong, C. G., Boucher, R., Nowaczynski, W., and Genest, J. (1966). *Mayo Clinic Proc.* **41** 433–452.

Struyk, C. B., Beerthuis, R. K., and van Dorp, D. A. (1967). *Nobel Symp. II, Prostaglandins, Stockholm, 1966* pp. 51–56. Almqvist & Wiksell, Stockholm.

Sullivan, T. J. (1966). *Brit. J. Pharmacol.* **26**, 678–685.

Suzuki, T., and Vogt, W. (1965). *Arch. Exptl. Pathol. Pharmakol.* **252**, 68–78.

Toh, C. C, (1963). *J. Physiol. (London)* **165**, 47–61.

Trapl, J. (1943). *Zentr. Gynaekol.* **67**, 547–550.

Uvnäs, B. (1965). *Arch. Exptl. Pathol. Pharmakol.* **250**, 164–166.

Vandelli, I. (1943). *Boll. Soc. Ital. Biol. Sper.* **18**, 73–77.

Van Demark, N. L., and Hays, R. L. (1954). *Fertility Sterility* **5**, 131–137.

Van Demark, N. L., and Moeller, A. N. (1951). *Am. J. Physiol.* **165**, 674–679.

van Dorp, D. A. (1966a). *Progr. Biochem. Pharmacol.* **3** (in press).

van Dorp, D. A. (1966b). *In* "Memoirs of the Society for Endocrinology" (V. R. Pickles and R. J. Fitzpatrick, eds.), No. 14, pp. 39–46. Cambridge Univ. Press, London and New York.

van Dorp, D. A., Beerthuis, R. K., Nugteren, D. H., and Vonkeman, H. (1964a). *Biochim. Biophys. Acta* **90**, 204–207.

van Dorp, D. A., Beerthuis, R. K., Nugteren, D. H., and Vonkeman, H. (1964b). *Nature* **203**, 839–841.

van Dorp, D. A., Jouvenaz, G. H., and Struijk, C. B. (1967). *Biochim. Biophys. Acta* **137**, 396–399.

Vane, J. R. (1957). *Brit. J. Pharmacol.* **12**, 344–349.

Vaughan, M. (1967). *Nobel Symp. II, Prostaglandins, Stockholm, 1966* pp. 139–142. Almqvist & Wiksell, Stockholm.

Vergroesen, A. J., de Boer, J., and Gottenbos, J. J. (1967). *Nobel Symp. II, Prostaglandins, Stockholm, 1966* pp. 211–218. Almqvist & Wiksell, Stockholm.

Vogt, W. (1949). *Arch. Exptl. Pathol. Pharmakol. Naunyn-Schmiedebergs* **206**, 1–11.

Vogt, W. (1956). *J. Physiol. (London)* **136**, 131–147.

Vogt, W. (1957). *J. Physiol. (London)* **137**, 154–167.

Vogt, W. (1958). *Pharmacol. Rev.* **10**, 407–435.

Vogt, W. (1960). *Arch. Exptl. Pathol. Pharmakol.* **240**, 134–139.

Vogt, W., Suzuki, T., and Babilli, S. (1966). *In* "Memoirs of the Society for Endocrinology" (V. R. Pickles and R. J. Fitzpatrick, eds.), No. 14, pp. 137–142. Cambridge Univ. Press, London and New York

Vogt, W., Suzuki, T., and Distelkötter, B. (1967). *Nobel Symp. II, Prostaglandins, Stockholm, 1966* pp. 237–240. Almqvist & Wiksell, Stockholm.

von Euler, U. S. (1934). *Arch. Exptl. Pathol. Pharmakol. Naunyn-Schmiedebergs* **175**, 78–84.

von Euler, U. S. (1935a). *Klin Wochschr.* **14**, 1182–1183.

von Euler, U. S. (1935b). *J. Physiol. (London)* **84**, 21P.

von Euler, U. S. (1936). *J. Physiol. (London)* **88**, 213–234.

von Euler, U. S. (1938). *J. Physiol. (London)* **93**, 129–143.

von Euler, U. S. (1939). *Skand. Arch. Physiol.* **81**, 65–80.

von Euler, U. S. (1961). *Harvey Lectures, Ser.* **55**, 43–65.

von Euler, U. S., and Hammarström, S. (1937). *Skand. Arch. Physiol.* **77**, 96–99.

Wallach, D. P. (1965). *Life Sci.* **4**, 361–364.

Wolfe, L. S., Coceani, F., and Spence, M. (1965). *Federation Proc.* **24**, 361.

Wolfe, L. S., Coceani, F., and Pace-Asciak, C. (1967). *Nobel Symp. II, Prostaglandins, Stockholm, 1966* pp. 265–276. Almqvist & Wiksell, Stockholm.

Subject Index

161